OXFORD

3C

Maths Links

C000051267

## Alf Ledsham

## Contents

# Homework Book

# OXFORD
UNIVERSITY PRESS

Great Clarendon Street, Oxford OX2 6DP

Oxford University Press is a department of the University of Oxford.
It furthers the University's objective of excellence in research, scholarship,
and education by publishing worldwide in

Oxford   New York

Auckland   Cape Town   Dar es Salaam   Hong Kong   Karachi
Kuala Lumpur   Madrid   Melbourne   Mexico City   Nairobi
New Delhi   Shanghai   Taipei   Toronto

With offices in

Argentina   Austria   Brazil   Chile   Czech Republic   France   Greece
Guatemala   Hungary   Italy   Japan   Poland   Portugal   Singapore
South Korea   Switzerland   Thailand   Turkey   Ukraine   Vietnam

British Library Cataloguing in Publication Data

Data available

ISBN-13: 9780-19-915299-5
10 9 8

Printed in Great Britain by Ashford Colour Press Ltd.

Paper used in the production of this book is a natural, recyclable product
made from wood grown in sustainable forests. The manufacturing process
conforms to the environmental regulations to the country of origin.

**example**

Calculate **a** $3 - -4$  **b** $35 \div -7$

. . . . . . . . . . . . . . . . . . . . . . . . . . . . . . . . . . . . .

**a** $3 - -4 = 3 + 4 = 7$ (Subtracting a negative number is the same as adding a positive number.)

**b** $35 \div -7 = -5$ (Dividing numbers with unlike signs gives a negative answer.)

**1** Place $<$ or $>$ between these pairs of numbers to show which one is larger.

**a** -9 and -10

**b** -8.9 and -9.1

**c** -7.2 and -7

**d** -4.8 and -5

**e** -6.81 and -6.79

**f** -5.3 and -5.32

**g** -8.49 and -8.5

**h** -2.841 and -2.839

**i** -0.48 and -0.482

**j** -0.958 and -0.96

**2** Calculate

**a** $12 + -9$     **b** $5 + -11$     **c** $-9 + 21$

**d** $-15 + 12$    **e** $-8 + -7$     **f** $-6 + -13$

**g** $15 - -6$     **h** $11 - -13$    **i** $-10 - 11$

**j** $-16 - 9$     **k** $-3 - -10$    **l** $-14 - -9$

**m** $15 + -3 - 7$  **n** $11 + -4 - -2$  **o** $5 + -12 - -3$

**3** Copy and complete

**a** the addition grid

**b** the subtraction grid. (Remember, when completing the subtraction grid, subtract each vertical from each horizontal.)

| + | 3 | 5 | 6 | 8 |
|---|---|---|---|---|
| -4 | -1 | | | |
| -6 | | | | |
| -9 | | | | |
| -12 | | | | |

| − | 4 | 6 | 10 | -4 | -6 | -10 |
|---|---|---|---|---|---|---|
| -3 | -7 | | | | | |
| -9 | | | | | | |
| -10 | | | | | | |
| -12 | | | | | | |

# 1b Factors and primes

example

List the prime numbers between 100 and 110.

. . . . . . . . . . . . . . . . . . . . . . . . . . . . . . . . . . . . . . . . . . . . . . .

The prime numbers between 100 and 110 are 101, 103, 107 and 109. These numbers have two and only two factors, namely themselves and one.

**1** Use divisibility tests to answer each of these questions. In each case, explain your answer and then check your answer by division.

**a** Is 5 a factor of 415?      **b** Is 3 a factor of 737?

**c** Is 7 a factor of 1645?      **d** Is 9 a factor of 1584?

**e** Is 11 a factor of 1010?      **f** Is 6 a factor of 1464?

**g** Is 18 a factor of 1998?      **h** Is 11 a factor of 1452?

**i** Is 15 a factor of 1680?      **j** Is 12 a factor of 1742?

**k** Is 24 a factor of 1824?      **l** Is 25 a factor of 1775?

**2** Write all the factors of

     **a** 270      **b** 640      **c** 1052

     **d** 1530      **e** 2310      **f** 1540

**3** Find all the prime numbers between 1 and 100. (There are 25 in all.)

**4** The Goldbach conjecture says that every even number greater than two can be written as the sum of two primes. Investigate this claim, do you think it is correct?

# 1c Prime factor decomposition

Write 90 as the product of its prime factors.

$90 = 2 \times 45 = 2 \times 3 \times 15 = 2 \times 3 \times 3 \times 5$ or $2 \times 3^2 \times 5$

**1** Work out the value of

   **a** $2^2 \times 3 \times 7$        **b** $2^2 \times 7 \times 11$

   **c** $2^2 \times 5 \times 13$      **d** $2^2 \times 3^2 \times 13$

   **e** $2^2 \times 5^2 \times 11$     **f** $2^2 \times 5 \times 7^2$

   **g** $2^3 \times 5^2 \times 7$      **h** $2^3 \times 5 \times 13$

**2** Write each of these numbers as the product of its prime factors.

   **a** 364             **b** 140

   **c** 132             **d** 300

   **e** 196             **f** 1300

   **g** 280             **h** 616

   **i** 720              **j** 1200

**3** List all the factors of each of these numbers.

   **a** 600             **b** 780

   **c** 360             **d** 1140

   **e** 1755           **f** 2340

**4 a** Find all numbers less than 30 that can be expressed as a product of three prime factors. (There are six in all.)

   **b** Find all numbers less than 60 which can be expressed as a product of four prime factors. (There are six in all.)

> **example**
>
> Find **a** the HCF **b** the LCM of 12 and 18.
> . . . . . . . . . . . . . . . . . . . . . . . . . . . . . . . . . . . . . . . . . .
> **a** $12 = 2 \times 6 = 2 \times \underline{2} \times \underline{3}$   $18 = 2 \times 9 = \underline{2} \times \underline{3} \times 3$   Therefore the
>    HCF is $2 \times 3$ or 6, because 2 and 3 are common to both.
> **b** The LCM is their product divided by their HCF which is
>    $12 \times 18 \div 6$ or 36.

**1** Find the HCF and LCM of

|   |   |   |   |
|---|---|---|---|
| **a** | 45 and 60 | **b** | 25 and 40 |
| **c** | 36 and 48 | **d** | 35 and 56 |
| **e** | 28 and 42 | **f** | 25, 50 and 60 |
| **g** | 24, 30 and 42 | **h** | 32, 40 and 56 |

**2** Find the HCF and LCM of

|   |   |   |   |
|---|---|---|---|
| **a** | 96 and 120 | **b** | 108 and 144 |
| **c** | 175 and 210 | **d** | 135 and 225 |
| **e** | 140 and 196 | **f** | 36, 54 and 90 |
| **g** | 72, 120 and 144 | **h** | 78, 130 and 208 |

**3** Cancel these fractions down. (You will find using the
HCF helpful for this.) Find which part has a different
answer from the other two.

**a i** $\frac{42}{56}$     **ii** $\frac{56}{84}$     **iii** $\frac{72}{96}$

**b i** $\frac{65}{78}$     **ii** $\frac{60}{75}$     **iii** $\frac{72}{90}$

**c i** $\frac{35}{60}$     **ii** $\frac{63}{108}$     **iii** $\frac{48}{90}$

**d i** $\frac{72}{81}$     **ii** $\frac{48}{54}$     **iii** $\frac{56}{64}$

**4** Work these out, giving each answer in its simplest
form.

**a** $\frac{7}{12} + \frac{4}{15}$     **b** $\frac{7}{20} + \frac{7}{12}$     **c** $\frac{17}{75} + \frac{27}{50}$     **d** $\frac{5}{6} + \frac{1}{15}$

**e** $\frac{11}{12} - \frac{7}{15}$     **f** $\frac{19}{20} - \frac{5}{12}$     **g** $\frac{67}{75} - \frac{13}{50}$     **h** $\frac{13}{15} - \frac{1}{6}$

**example**

Calculate **a** $1.1^2$      **b** $1.3^3$      **c** $\sqrt{900}$      **d** $\sqrt[3]{1000}$

**a** $1.1^2 = 1.1 \times 1.1 = 1.21$      **b** $1.3^3 = 1.3 \times 1.3 \times 1.3 = 2.197$
**c** $\sqrt{900} = 30$ because      **d** $\sqrt[3]{1000} = 10$ because
     $30 \times 30 = 900$                   $10 \times 10 \times 10 = 1000$

**1** Calculate
   **a** $20^2$      **b** $16^2$      **c** $13^2$      **d** $26^2$
   **e** $31^2$      **f** $1.7^2$      **g** $3.2^2$      **h** $0.9^2$
   **i** $0.6^2$      **j** $(-10)^2$      **k** $(-12)^2$      **l** $(-25)^2$

**2** Find the square root of
   **a** 196      **b** 441      **c** 576      **d** 784      **e** 289

**3** Calculate
   **a** $3^3$      **b** $6^3$      **c** $9^3$      **d** $30^3$
   **e** $50^3$      **f** $1.5^3$      **g** $0.8^3$      **h** $0.3^3$
   **i** $0.1^3$      **j** $(-4)^3$      **k** $(-7)^3$      **l** $(-10)^3$

**4** Find the cube root of
   **a** 64      **b** 125      **c** 512      **d** 64 000
   **e** 0.729      **f** 0.343      **g** 0.125      **h** 0.064
   **i** 1 000 000      **j** -27      **k** -216      **l** -1

**5 a** Find the square root of these correct to 1 dp.
     **i** 1000      **ii** 500      **iii** 320      **iv** 90
   **b** Find the cube root of these correct to 1 dp.
     **i** 100      **ii** 900      **iii** 90      **iv** 5

**6 a** A square room has an area of $14.44 \text{ m}^2$.
     Find its side length.
   **b** This storage tank is a cube. Its volume
     is $1.331 \text{ m}^3$. Find its side length.

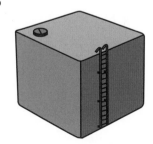

**example**

Simplify **a** $9^4 \times 9^2$ **b** $10^8 \div 10^5$
leaving your answers as a single power of the number.
· · · · · · · · · · · · · · · · · · · · · · · · · · · · · · · · · · · · · · · · · · ·

**a** $9^4 \times 9^2 = 9^6$ because the powers are added for a multiplication.

**b** $10^8 \div 10^5 = 10^3$ because the powers are subtracted for a division.

**1** Calculate these powers.

| | | | |
|---|---|---|---|
| **a** $4^3$ | **b** $11^3$ | **c** $2^4$ | **d** $3^4$ |
| **e** $2^5$ | **f** $2^8$ | **g** $10^4$ | **h** $10^6$ |
| **i** $3^7$ | **j** $5^5$ | **k** $2^1$ | **l** $5^1$ |
| **m** $1000^1$ | **n** $5^0$ | **o** $10^0$ | **p** $10\,000^0$ |

**2** Put these numbers in order from smallest to largest.

$12^3 \quad 3^7 \quad 2^{10} \quad 5^5 \quad 7^4$

**3** Find the value of the letter in each equation.

**a** $3^x = 243$      **b** $4^y = 16384$

**c** $2^z = 512$      **d** $2^t = 2048$

**e** $7^u = 2401$      **f** $10^w = 100\,000$

**g** $8^m = 32768$      **h** $100^n = 1$

**4** Simplify each of these, leaving your answer as a single power of the number.

| | | |
|---|---|---|
| **a** $3^4 \times 3^3$ | **b** $5^2 \times 5^3$ | **c** $4^6 \times 4$ |
| **d** $4^2 \times 4^3 \times 4^3$ | **e** $5^3 \times 5^2 \times 5$ | **f** $9^5 \times 9^2 \times 9^0$ |
| **g** $8^7 \div 8^4$ | **h** $10^9 \div 10^3$ | **i** $9^4 \div 9^3$ |
| **j** $(7^2 \times 7^3 \times 7^2) \div 7^4$ | **k** $(8^5 \times 8^2 \times 8) \div 8^3$ | **l** $(6^4 \times 6^3 \times 6^0) \div 6^7$ |

example

Change 0.03 tonnes to **a** kilograms **b** grams.

**a** $0.03\,t = 0.03 \times 1000\,kg = 30\,kg$

**b** $30\,kg = 30 \times 1000\,g$
$= 30\,000\,g$

**1** Copy and complete the tables. (A hint to help you with part **b**: ha stands for hectares, 1 ha = 10 000 m²)

**a**

| mm | cm | m | km |
|---|---|---|---|
| 2 000 000 | | | |
| 1 500 000 | | | |
| | 400 000 | | |
| | 120 000 | | |
| | | 7500 | |
| | | 3500 | |
| | | | 7 |
| | | | 2.25 |
| | | | 0.3 |

**b**

| cm² | m² | ha |
|---|---|---|
| 9 000 000 | | |
| 3 500 000 | | |
| | 70 000 | |
| | 5000 | |
| | | 0.2 |
| 40 000 | | 0.0004 |

**2** Copy and complete the tables.

**a**

| ml | cl | litres |
|---|---|---|
| 5000 | | |
| 12 000 | | |
| | 1700 | |
| | 350 | |
| | | 10.5 |
| | | 0.6 |
| | | 0.07 |

**b**

| g | kg | t |
|---|---|---|
| 3 000 000 | | |
| 8 500 000 | | |
| | | 11 |
| | | 2.5 |
| | 900 | |
| | 750 | |
| | | 0.05 |
| | | 0.002 |

example

**a** Abdul's mass is 11 stones. Convert this to **i** pounds
**ii** kilograms. (1 kg ≈ 2.2 lb)
**b** Abdul's height is 170 cm. Convert this to **i** inches
**ii** feet and inches. (1 in ≈ 2.5 cm)

. . . . . . . . . . . . . . . . . . . . . . . . . . . . . . . . . . . . . . . . . . . . . . . . . . . . . . .

**a i** 11 stones = 11 × 14 or 154 pounds (lb)
**ii** 154 lb = 154 ÷ 2.2 or 70 kg
**b i** 170 cm = 170 ÷ 2.5 or 68 in
**ii** 68 in = 68 ÷ 12 ft; 68 ÷ 12 = 5 remainder 8, therefore
170 cm = 5 ft 8 in

**1 a** James, Peter and Ray are three bothers and their
masses are 9 st 6 lb, 7 st 12 lb and 5 st 7 lb. Convert
these masses to **i** pounds **ii** kilograms.
**b** Hita, Tarani and Sameera are three sisters and
their masses are 45 kg, 30 kg and 25 kg. Convert
these masses to **i** pounds **ii** stones and pounds.

**2 a** Jean, Rita and Barbara are three sisters and their
heights are 5 ft 4 in, 5 ft and 4 ft 6 in. Convert these
heights to **i** inches **ii** centimetres.
**b** Aleksy, Jan and Raf are three brothers and
their heights are 155 cm, 145 cm and 130 cm. Convert
these heights to **i** inches **ii** feet and inches.

**3** The table shows the capacity of the petrol tanks of six cars.
Copy and complete the table. (1 gallon ≈ 4.5 litres. )

| | Seb's car | Anne's car | Lali's car | Ronnie's car | Julian's car | Nicola's car |
|---|---|---|---|---|---|---|
| Tank capacity (litres) | 36 | 44.1 | 50.4 | | | |
| Tank capacity (gallons) | | | | 9 | 8.4 | 11.8 |

**example**

Find the area of the shape.

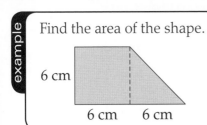
6 cm
6 cm 6 cm

The shape is made up of a square and a triangle, therefore the area is $(6 \times 6) + \frac{1}{2}(6 \times 6) = 36 + 18 = 54\,cm^2$.

**1** Calculate the perimeter and area of each of these rectangles. State the units of your anwers.

**a**
15 cm
10 cm

**b**
18 cm
7 cm

**2** Calculate the perimeter and area of each of these shapes which are made from rectangles. State the units of your answers.

**a**
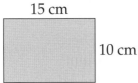
12 cm
2 cm
6 cm
2 cm

**b**
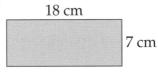
15 cm
3 cm
6 cm
3 cm

**3** Calculate the area of each of these triangles.

**a**
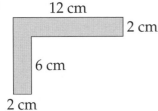
1.5 m
1.6 m

**b**
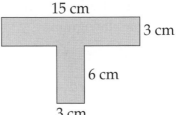
0.6 m
0.9 m

**4** Calculate the unknown length in each of these shapes.

**a**
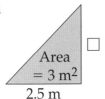
Area = 3 m²
2.5 m
□

**b**

21 cm
Area = 252 cm²
□

**example**

Find the area of **a** the parallelogram **b** the trapezium.

**a**

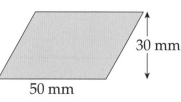

50 mm

30 mm

**b**

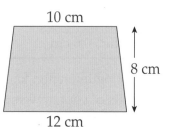

10 cm

8 cm

12 cm

**a** The area of a parallelogram = base × vertical height
$$= 50 \times 30 = 1500 \, \text{mm}^2$$

**b** The area of a trapezium $= \frac{1}{2} \times ($ sum of parallel sides$)$
$\times$ vertical height $= \frac{1}{2} \times (10 + 12) \times 8 = 88 \, \text{cm}^2$

**1** Calculate the perimeter and area of
   **a** the parallelogram       **b** the isosceles trapezium.

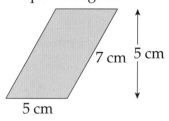

7 cm   5 cm

5 cm

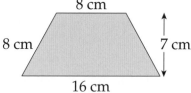

8 cm

8 cm       7 cm

16 cm

**2** Find the unknown lengths in these parallelograms.

**a**

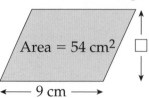

Area = 54 cm²   ☐

← 9 cm →

**b**

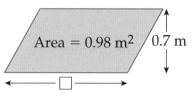

Area = 0.98 m²   0.7 m

← ☐ →

**example**

A circle has a radius of 7 cm.
Find **a** its diameter
**b** its circumference.

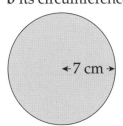

←7 cm→

**a** The diameter
= 2 × radius
= 2 × 7 = 14 cm
**b** The circumference
= π × diameter
= 3.14 × 14 cm
= 43.96 cm

**1** Copy and complete the table.

| Radius | Diameter | Circumference |
|---|---|---|
| | 8 cm | |
| | 5 cm | |
| 6 cm | | |
| 100 mm | | |
| | 18 cm | |
| | 30 mm | |
| 12.5 cm | | |
| 0.75 m | | |

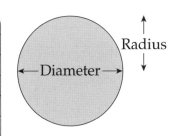

Radius

←Diameter→

**2** Mumbi's garden has a circular pond of diameter
10.5 m. If she walks around the edge of it, how
far does she walk?

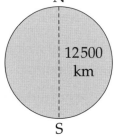

←10.5 m→

**3** If a tunnel could be bored from the
North Pole to the South Pole it
would be 12 500 km long. What is
the circumference of the Earth?

N

12 500
km

S

example

A circle has a radius of 15 cm. Find its area.

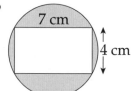

15 cm

The area $= \pi \times (\text{radius})^2$
$= 3.14 \times 15^2$
$= 706.5 \text{ cm}^2$

**1** Copy and complete the table.

| Diameter | | | 4 cm | 10 cm | | | 100 mm | 0.8 m | | |
|---|---|---|---|---|---|---|---|---|---|---|
| Radius | 3 cm | 2.5 cm | | | 60 mm | 80 mm | | | | 0.01 m | 0.05 m |
| Area of circle | | | | | | | | | | | |

**2** Find the area of the shaded regions in each of these shapes.

**a**

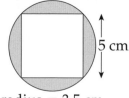

5 cm

radius = 3.5 cm

**b**

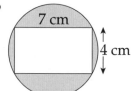

7 cm

4 cm

radius = 4 cm

**c**

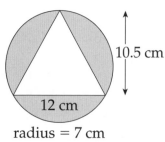

10.5 cm

12 cm

radius = 7 cm

**d**

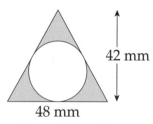

42 mm

48 mm

radius = 14 mm

**3** The minute hand of a clock is 12 cm long. Find the area that it covers in 1 hour.

**4** A compact disc has a diameter of 12 cm. Find its area.

# 3a Two or more events

A fair coin is thrown twice.
**a** List the possible outcomes.
**b** What is the probability of getting one head and one tail?

**a** Head head, head tail, tail head, tail tail
**b** All four outcomes are equally probable and there are two ways of getting one head and one tail. The probability is therefore $\frac{2}{4}$ or $\frac{1}{2}$.

**1** Two tetrahedral dice are thrown. Copy and complete the tables, one for the possible outcomes, one for the scores (the sum of the two dice in each outcome) and one for the probability of each possible score.

|   | 1 | 2 | 3 | 4 |
|---|---|---|---|---|
| 1 | 1,1 | 1,2 |   |   |
| 2 |   |   |   |   |
| 3 |   |   |   |   |
| 4 |   |   |   |   |

| Sum | 1 | 2 | 3 | 4 |
|-----|---|---|---|---|
| 1 | 2 | 3 |   |   |
| 2 |   |   |   |   |
| 3 |   |   |   |   |
| 4 |   |   |   |   |

| Score | 2 | 3 | 4 | 5 | 6 | 7 | 8 |
|-------|---|---|---|---|---|---|---|
| Probability | $\frac{1}{16}$ |   |   |   |   |   |   |

Find the probability that the score is **a** a prime number **b** a multiple of 3 **c** a factor of 8.

Eli writes the letters of her name on three cards and puts them in a bag. She picks out one card and notes the letter before putting it back in the bag. She then picks out a second letter.

**a** Show the possible combinations of the two letters in a tree diagram.

**b** What is the probability that Eli picks only one vowel?

**a**  First   Second   **b**  $\frac{4}{9}$  (EL, LE, LI, IL)

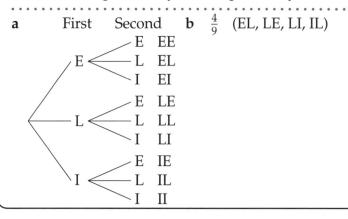

**1** Sam writes the letters of his name on three cards and puts them in a bag. He picks out one card and notes the letter before putting it back in the bag. He then picks out a second letter.

**a** Show the possible combination of letters in a tree diagram.

**b i** What is the probability that Sam picks a vowel?

**ii** What is the probability that Sam doesn't pick a vowel?

**2** Repeat question **1** but now assume that the first card is not put back in the bag.

# 3c Mutually exclusive outcomes

**1** Are the following pairs of events mutually exclusive?
  **a i** blizzards blanket the country in a meter of snow
  **ii** you go to school the next day.
  **b** The sum of the scores showing on four dice is
  **i** prime
  **ii** a triangular number.
  **c i** you can see a rainbow
  **ii** it is snowing.

**2** Four events are defined using the scores on two dice;
  A  both scores are prime
  B  the scores differ by one
  C  the sum of the scores is a multiple of four
  D  the difference in the scores is four or more.

  Say whether each of the six possible pairs of events is mutually exclusive or not.

**3** A three sided spinner, labelled 1 2 3, is spun twice.
  **a** Show the possible outcomes on
  **i** a sample space diagram
  **ii** a tree diagram
  **b** Calculate the following probabilities
  **i** the sum of the scores is odd
  **ii** the two scores are the same
  **c** Use your results from part **b** to calculate the following probabilities
  **i** the sum of the scores is even
  **ii** the two scores are different.

**example**

Bob plays in goal for his football team and one season his team had 15 penalties given against them.
If he saved 6 of them what is the probability that he will save any one penalty?

The probability is $\frac{6}{15}$ or $\frac{2}{5}$.

**1** Rajmeet asks 120 Year 11 pupils what they are going to do next year. Fifty say they are staying at school, thirty say they are going to a college and forty say that they are going to find a job. Using these figures, find the probability that a Year 11 pupil **a** stays at school **b** goes to a college **c** finds a job.

**2** 1200 people in a small town were asked how they were going to vote in a forthcoming general election. 560 said Labour, 440 said Conservative and 200 said Liberal Democrat. Use these details to estimate the probability that anyone chosen at random would vote
**a** Labour **b** Conservative **c** Liberal Democrat.

**3** A commuter train is due in London at 8:45 a.m. The arrival times for a certain 30-day month are given.

| 8:43 | 8:42 | 8:44 | 8:46 | 8:45 | 8:43 | 8:45 | 8:47 | 8:50 | 8:48 | 8:41 | 8:52 | 8:49 | 8:45 | 8:44 |
|------|------|------|------|------|------|------|------|------|------|------|------|------|------|------|
| 8:41 | 8:42 | 8:46 | 8:47 | 8:49 | 8:43 | 8:45 | 8:44 | 8:53 | 8:49 | 8:40 | 8:45 | 8:47 | 8:45 | 8:44 |

From these data what is the probability that the train will be **a** late **b** more than 5 min late **c** early **d** on time?

**4** A football club's record over 20 matches is shown.

| Goals for | 3 | 1 | 3 | 1 | 2 | 0 | 2 | 4 | 3 | 1 | 0 | 5 | 2 | 2 | 1 | 1 | 4 | 5 | 2 | 3 |
|-----------|---|---|---|---|---|---|---|---|---|---|---|---|---|---|---|---|---|---|---|---|
| Goals against | 0 | 2 | 2 | 1 | 0 | 1 | 2 | 3 | 1 | 3 | 0 | 2 | 1 | 0 | 3 | 4 | 0 | 3 | 3 | 3 |

From these data estimate the probability that they
**a** win a game **b** lose a game **c** draw a game
**d** score no goals **e** have no goals scored against them.

example

Some street decorations include some slow flashing lights and the operating equipment is designed to give a probability of 0.6 that a light will be on. A light-operated timer, however, was placed near to a light for 3 hours and recorded that the time it was on for was 1 h 57 min. Find the probability from these figures and comment on the result.

. . . . . . . . . . . . . . . . . . . . . . . . . . . . . . . . . . . . . . . . . .

1 h 57 min = 117 min and 3 h = 180 min. The probability is therefore $117 \div 180 = \frac{13}{20}$ or 0.65.
This is fairly close to the claimed probability.

**1** In a cafe there is a gaming machine that is operated by £1 coins. These probabilties are claimed by the manufacturer for the possible outcomes.

| Outcome | Win £2 | Win £1 | £1 coin returned | Lose your £1 coin |
|---|---|---|---|---|
| Probability | $\frac{1}{10}$ | $\frac{1}{5}$ | $\frac{3}{10}$ | $\frac{2}{5}$ |

A fair trading officer doubts these figures and tests the machine 60 times. Copy and complete the table and comment on his results.

| Outcome | Win £2 | Win £1 | £1 coin returned | Lose the £1 coin |
|---|---|---|---|---|
| Number of times | 5 | 9 | 16 | 30 |
| Experimental probability | | | | |

**2** In a series of games a pair of tetrahedronal dice are thrown 80 times and Marcus records the results. Copy and complete his table.

| Score | 2 | 3 | 4 | 5 | 6 | 7 | 8 |
|---|---|---|---|---|---|---|---|
| Number of times | 2 | 8 | 16 | 24 | 16 | 8 | 6 |
| Experimental probability | | | | | | | |
| Theoretical probability | | | | | | | |

Marcus thinks that one or both of the dice must be biased. Would you agree?

A coin is tossed six times and the number of heads is recorded. The experiment is repeated ten times. The results of the repeated experiment are shown on the left and a simulation, using $P(\text{head}) = 0.5$, is shown on the right. Do you think that the coin used in the experiment is biased? Explain your reasoning.

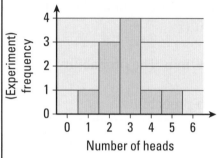

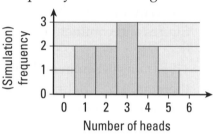

Probably not, because both frequency diagrams show a fairly symmetric pattern with the expected number of three heads per experiment having the highest frequency.

**1** A tetrahedronal dice is thrown 5 times and the number of fours is recorded. The experiment is repeated 20 times over. The results of the repeated experiment are shown on the left and a simulation, using $P$ (of a 4) $= 0.25$ is shown on the right. Do you think that the dice used in the experiment is biased? Explain your reasoning.

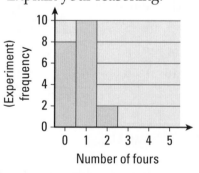

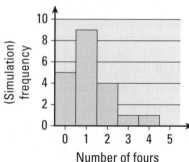

# 4a Fractions and decimals

Put these fractions in order from lowest to highest. $\frac{11}{24}$ $\frac{37}{80}$ $\frac{9}{20}$

$\frac{11}{24} = 0.4583.....$   $\frac{37}{80} = 0.4625$   $\frac{9}{20} = 0.45$

Therefore in ascending order the list is $\frac{9}{20}$ $\frac{11}{24}$ $\frac{37}{80}$.

**1** Write these decimals as fractions in their simplest form.

**a** 0.6 **b** 0.16 **c** 0.48 **d** 0.06 **e** 0.55

**f** 1.32 **g** 2.96 **h** 4.28 **i** 3.45 **j** 4.4

**2** Change these fractions to decimals without using a calculator.

**a** $\frac{4}{5}$ **b** $\frac{6}{25}$ **c** $\frac{14}{25}$ **d** $\frac{1}{50}$ **e** $\frac{7}{20}$

**f** $\frac{21}{5}$ **g** $\frac{34}{25}$ **h** $\frac{71}{25}$ **i** $\frac{103}{20}$ **j** $\frac{91}{20}$

**3** Change these fractions to decimals by any convenient method. Give your answer to 4 dp where appropriate.

**a** $\frac{7}{16}$ **b** $\frac{9}{40}$ **c** $\frac{25}{80}$ **d** $\frac{15}{32}$ **e** $\frac{3}{7}$

**f** $\frac{5}{7}$ **g** $\frac{16}{21}$ **h** $\frac{24}{35}$ **i** $\frac{5}{12}$ **j** $\frac{7}{12}$

**k** $\frac{11}{8}$ **l** $\frac{21}{8}$ **m** $\frac{51}{16}$ **n** $\frac{87}{40}$ **o** $\frac{41}{32}$

**4** Place $<$ or $>$ between these pairs to show which term is larger.

**a** $\frac{1}{7}$ and $\frac{3}{20}$ **b** $\frac{6}{7}$ and $\frac{17}{20}$

**c** $\frac{8}{15}$ and $\frac{13}{25}$ **d** $\frac{23}{25}$ and $\frac{11}{12}$

**e** $\frac{13}{15}$ and $\frac{7}{8}$ **f** $\frac{14}{15}$ and $\frac{19}{20}$

**g** $\frac{14}{25}$ and $\frac{19}{35}$ **h** $\frac{19}{40}$ and $\frac{7}{15}$

**i** $\frac{15}{32}$ and $\frac{22}{45}$

**5** Put the lengths of the four avenues in order starting with the smallest.

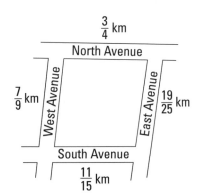

## 4b Adding and subtracting fractions

Calculate **a** $1\frac{1}{15} + \frac{1}{10}$       **b** $2\frac{1}{10} - \frac{7}{20}$

Give your answers as fractions in their simplest form.

**a** $1\frac{1}{15} + \frac{1}{10} = \frac{16}{15} + \frac{1}{10} = \frac{32}{30} + \frac{3}{30} = \frac{35}{30} = \frac{7}{6} = 1\frac{1}{6}$

**b** $2\frac{1}{10} - \frac{7}{20} = \frac{21}{10} - \frac{7}{20} = \frac{42}{20} - \frac{7}{20} = \frac{35}{20} = \frac{7}{4} = 1\frac{3}{4}$

**1** Calculate

   **a** $\frac{5}{14} + \frac{3}{14}$      **b** $\frac{7}{10} + \frac{1}{10}$      **c** $\frac{4}{15} + \frac{8}{15}$

   **d** $\frac{7}{12} + \frac{1}{12}$      **e** $\frac{13}{15} - \frac{4}{15}$      **f** $\frac{11}{20} - \frac{3}{20}$

   **g** $\frac{23}{30} - \frac{11}{30}$      **h** $\frac{11}{12} - \frac{7}{12}$      **i** $1\frac{5}{6} - 1\frac{1}{6}$

   **j** $2\frac{9}{20} - 1\frac{1}{20}$      **k** $2\frac{3}{20} + 1\frac{7}{20}$      **l** $3\frac{1}{12} + 1\frac{7}{12}$

**2** Calculate

   **a** $\frac{1}{6} + \frac{8}{15}$      **b** $\frac{5}{12} + \frac{2}{15}$      **c** $\frac{3}{10} + \frac{8}{15}$

   **d** $\frac{3}{5} + \frac{3}{20}$      **e** $\frac{4}{5} - \frac{11}{20}$      **f** $\frac{13}{15} - \frac{1}{6}$

   **g** $\frac{14}{15} - \frac{1}{10}$      **h** $\frac{11}{12} - \frac{4}{15}$      **i** $\frac{7}{15} + \frac{5}{6}$

   **j** $\frac{11}{20} + \frac{7}{12}$      **k** $\frac{3}{4} + \frac{13}{20}$      **l** $\frac{5}{6} + \frac{11}{12}$

**3** Calculate

   **a** $1\frac{1}{6} + 1\frac{2}{15}$      **b** $1\frac{1}{15} + 2\frac{1}{10}$      **c** $2\frac{1}{5} + 1\frac{11}{20}$

   **d** $3\frac{1}{10} + 2\frac{3}{20}$      **e** $3\frac{3}{5} + 2\frac{1}{15}$      **f** $3\frac{3}{10} - 1\frac{2}{15}$

   **g** $2\frac{5}{6} - 1\frac{3}{10}$      **h** $3\frac{2}{5} - 2\frac{3}{20}$      **i** $2\frac{4}{5} - 1\frac{7}{15}$

   **j** $2\frac{3}{4} - 1\frac{11}{12}$      **k** $3\frac{1}{3} - 2\frac{7}{12}$      **l** $1\frac{5}{6} - \frac{14}{15}$

**4** Find the distance from
   **a** Albury to Gomshall
   **b** Gomshall to Abinger
     Hammer.

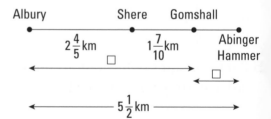

**example**

Calculate **a** $1\frac{2}{9} \times \frac{3}{4}$       **b** $\frac{7}{8} \div \frac{9}{16}$

Give your answers as fractions in their simplest form.

**a** $1\frac{2}{9} \times \frac{3}{4} = \frac{11}{9} \times \frac{3}{4} = \frac{33}{36} = \frac{11}{12}$      **b** $\frac{7}{8} \div \frac{9}{16} = \frac{7}{8} \times \frac{16}{9} = \frac{112}{72} = \frac{14}{9} = 1\frac{5}{9}$

**1** Calculate

**a** $3 \times \frac{4}{15}$    **b** $2 \times \frac{3}{16}$    **c** $4 \times \frac{3}{20}$    **d** $5 \times \frac{4}{25}$    **e** $2 \times \frac{5}{18}$

**f** $3 \times \frac{7}{12}$    **g** $2 \times \frac{11}{12}$    **h** $5 \times \frac{7}{20}$    **i** $4 \times \frac{7}{16}$    **j** $3 \times \frac{8}{15}$

**k** $3 \div \frac{6}{7}$    **l** $2 \div \frac{4}{15}$    **m** $4 \div \frac{8}{9}$    **n** $5 \div \frac{15}{16}$    **o** $3 \div \frac{12}{25}$

**2** Calculate

**a** $\frac{3}{4} \times \frac{6}{7}$      **b** $\frac{5}{6} \times \frac{9}{11}$      **c** $\frac{3}{8} \times \frac{12}{25}$

**d** $\frac{7}{10} \times \frac{4}{15}$      **e** $\frac{7}{12} \times \frac{9}{10}$      **f** $\frac{8}{15} \times \frac{9}{20}$

**g** $\frac{9}{20} \times \frac{16}{27}$      **h** $\frac{12}{25} \times \frac{15}{16}$      **i** $\frac{8}{15} \times \frac{9}{10}$

**j** $\frac{10}{21} \times \frac{14}{25}$      **k** $\frac{14}{15} \times \frac{9}{35}$      **l** $\frac{5}{6} \times \frac{9}{25}$

**m** $\frac{7}{15} \times \frac{10}{21}$      **n** $\frac{8}{9} \times \frac{3}{16}$      **o** $\frac{3}{5} \div \frac{9}{10}$

**p** $\frac{8}{15} \div \frac{16}{21}$      **q** $\frac{9}{20} \div \frac{27}{50}$      **r** $\frac{12}{25} \div \frac{8}{15}$

**s** $\frac{4}{21} \div \frac{6}{35}$      **t** $\frac{18}{25} \div \frac{27}{40}$      **u** $\frac{9}{10} \div \frac{27}{40}$

**3** It is $12\frac{1}{2}$ km from Birmingham to Halesowen, if I walk $\frac{3}{5}$ of the way how far do I walk?

**4** A film show lasts for $2\frac{1}{4}$ hours, but I arrive late and only see $\frac{2}{3}$ of it. For how long was I in the cinema?

**5** A supermarket manager has $13\frac{1}{2}$ kg of flour and he packs it into $\frac{3}{4}$ kg bags. How many bags does he fill?

**6** A coal merchant packs $2\frac{1}{4}$ tonnes of coal into bags which each hold $\frac{1}{20}$ of a tonne. How many bags does he fill?

**a** Increase £56 by 5%.    **b** Decrease 160 km by 2.5%.

. . . . . . . . . . . . . . . . . . . . . . . . . . . . . . . . . . . . . . . . . . .

**a** The amount after the increase $= 56 \times \frac{105}{100} = £58.80$

**b** The amount after the decrease $= 160 \times \frac{97.5}{100} = 156$ km

**1** Calculate these percentages. Find which part has a
different answer from the other two.

| | | |
|---|---|---|
| **a i** 15% of £80 | **ii** 25% of £56 | **iii** 48% of £25 |
| **b i** 16% of £55 | **ii** 17% of £50 | **iii** 22% of £40 |
| **c i** 35% of 20 km | **ii** 25% of 30 km | **iii** 15% of 50 km |
| **d i** 25% of 45 m | **ii** 9% of 125 m | **iii** 23% of 50 m |

**2** Calculate these increases.

| | |
|---|---|
| **a** £50 by 6% | **b** £480 by 7.5% |
| **c** 56 km by 2.5% | **d** 360 g by 12.5% |

**3** Calculate these decreases.

| | |
|---|---|
| **a** £60 by 15% | **b** £120 by 7.5% |
| **c** 96 m by 35% | **d** 160 kg by 4.5% |

**4** The train fare from my local station to London is £42
and the journey time is 1 h 50 min. A new service
starts for which the fare is 15% more, but the journey
time is 10% less. Find
**a** the fare
**b** the journey time for the new service.

**5** Mr. Sidhu wants to buy a new car which costs £15 000.
He can not afford that but he is given two hire
purchase options. The first is to pay a 15% deposit
and then 12 monthly payments of £1125. The second
is to pay a 16% deposit and then 12 monthly payments
of £1110. Which is the better option and by how much?

# 4e Percentage problems

**example**

**a** Bill has had to take a pay cut. His weekly wage is now £266 after a 5% decrease. What was his wage originally?

**b** Hazel is putting on weight. Her weight is now 78 kg after a 4% increase. What was her weight originally?

. . . . . . . . . . . . . . . . . . . . . . . . . . . . . . . . . . . . . . . . . . . . . . . .

**a** Original wage $= \frac{100}{95} \times 266 = £280$

**b** Original weight $= \frac{100}{104} \times 78 = 75$ kg

**1** A food manufacturer has decided to sell its products in larger packets. Copy and complete the table.

| Product | Mass of new packet | Percentage increase | Mass of old packet | Actual increase |
|---------|--------------------|---------------------|--------------------|-----------------|
| 'Frooty' sweets | 186 g | 20% | | |
| Selected biscuits | 368 g | 15% | | |
| Corn flakes | 477 g | 6% | | |
| Assorted chocolates | 459 g | 12.5% | | |
| Jar of jam | 559 g | 7.5% | | |
| Dried milk | 455 g | 25% | | |
| Bag of flour | | 20% | | 85 g |
| Packet of mints | | 15% | | 27 g |
| Carton of fruit juice | | 12.5% | | 59 g |
| Carton of milk | | 8% | | 44 g |

**2** One day Tom buys an electric drill when the shop offers a 20% discount. The next day Jake buys an identical drill but the discount is then 25%. If Tom paid £4 more than Jake, what was the original price of the drill?

**example**

A bus starts its journey with 20 passengers on board. After its first stop it is carrying 25 passengers and after its second stop only 15. Find **a** the percentage increase in passengers after the first stop **b** the percentage decrease in passengers after the second stop.

........................................................

**a** The actual increase $= 25 - 20 = 5$. Therefore the percentage increase $= \frac{5}{20} \times 100\% = 25\%$

**b** The actual decrease $= 25 - 15 = 10$. Therefore the percentage decrease $= \frac{10}{25} \times 100\% = 40\%$

**1** A village primary school has 120 pupils. 30 of them walk to school, 48 are brought by car, 36 come on the school bus and 6 of them cycle. Convert these figures to percentages of the total.

**2** The table shows the pay rises that eight people have received. Copy and complete the table.

| | Fred | Bob | Mary | Ravinda | Ayo | Jisanne | Shani | Candace |
|---|---|---|---|---|---|---|---|---|
| Old wage | £240 | £225 | £205 | £196 | £194.50 | £256.80 | £200 | £256 |
| New wage | £252 | £234 | £221.40 | £201.88 | £213.95 | £295.32 | £215 | £288 |
| Increase (£) | | | | | | | | |
| Increase (%) | | | | | | | | |

**3** The table shows how eight members of a keep fit club lost weight during a certain month. Copy and complete the table.

| | Sharon | Kanika | Layla | Isaac | Ronnie | Jacob | Wayne | Simone |
|---|---|---|---|---|---|---|---|---|
| Mass at start of the month (kg) | 70 | 50 | 60 | 75 | 75 | 80 | 80 | 72 |
| Mass at end of the month (kg) | 63 | 48 | 57 | 69 | 66 | 78 | 74 | 63 |
| Mass loss (kg) | | | | | | | | |
| Mass loss (%) | | | | | | | | |

## 5a Indices in algebra

Calculate

**a** $7^{-3}$        **b** $a^2 - b^2$ if $a = 5$ and $b = -6$

. . . . . . . . . . . . . . . . . . . . . . . . . . . . . . . . . . . . . . . . . . . . . . . . . . . . . . . . .

**a** $7^{-3} = \frac{1}{7^3} = \frac{1}{343}$    **b** $a^2 - b^2 = 5^2 - (-6)^2 = 25 - 36 = -11$

**1** Evaluate each of these expressions.

   **a** $3^3$       **b** $2^5$       **c** $10^4$       **d** $4^4$       **e** $(-2)^2$       **f** $(-2)^4$

   **g** $(-5)^3$       **h** $\left(\frac{3}{4}\right)^2$       **i** $\left(\frac{2}{3}\right)^4$       **j** $\left(\frac{5}{6}\right)^3$       **k** $\left(\frac{4}{5}\right)^4$       **l** $\left(\frac{1}{10}\right)^6$

**2** Evaluate each of these expressing the answer as
   a fraction.

   **a** $2^{-3}$       **b** $6^{-3}$       **c** $5^{-4}$       **d** $3^{-4}$       **e** $4^{-3}$       **f** $\left(\frac{1}{2}\right)^{-4}$

   **g** $\left(\frac{1}{3}\right)^{-2}$       **h** $\left(\frac{5}{6}\right)^{-2}$       **i** $\left(\frac{3}{4}\right)^{-3}$       **j** $\left(\frac{3}{5}\right)^{-3}$       **k** $\left(\frac{7}{10}\right)^{-2}$       **l** $\left(\frac{1}{10}\right)^{-5}$

**3** Evaluate each of these expressions if $x = 3$ and $y = -4$.

   **a** $xy$       **b** $5xy$       **c** $y^2$       **d** $8y^2$       **e** $xy^2$       **f** $x^2y$

   **g** $4x^3$       **h** $(3x)^3$       **i** $(5x)^2$       **j** $y^3$       **k** $6y^3$       **l** $(3y)^2$

   **m** $x^2 + y$       **n** $x^2 + y^2$       **o** $x^2 - y$       **p** $x - y^2$       **q** $x^2y^2$

**4 a** The volume of a sphere is very closely equal
   to $\frac{88}{21}r^3$. Use this formula to find the volume
   if $r$ is equal to **i** 10.5 cm **ii** 5.25 cm **iii** 4.2 cm
   **iv** 0.21 m.

   **b** The volume $(V)$ of a cylinder is very closely
   equal to $\frac{22}{7}r^2h$.

   Copy and complete the table using this
   formula.

| $r =$ | 14 cm | 12 mm | 0.6 m | 0.21 m |
|-------|-------|-------|-------|--------|
| $h =$ | 30 cm | 28 mm | 1.05 m | 0.5 m |
| $V =$ |       |       |       |        |

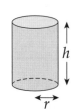

## 5b Collecting like terms including powers

Simplify **a** $3m^2 + 5m + m^2 - 4m$     **b** $\dfrac{(8u + 12u^2)}{4u}$

· · · · · · · · · · · · · · · · · · · · · · · · · · · · · · · · · · · · · · · · · · · · · · · · ·

**a** $3m^2 + 5m + m^2 - 4m = 4m^2 + m$     **b** $\dfrac{(8u + 12u^2)}{4u} = 2 + 3u$

For questions **1** to **3** simplify each expression by collecting like terms.

**1 a** $3x + 2x + 5x$    **b** $7y + 9y - 4y$    **c** $8z + 2z - 7z$
   **d** $10s - 6s + 8s$    **e** $12t - 5t + 2t$    **f** $15u - 8u - 3u$

**2 a** $3u + 5v + 7u + 2v$      **b** $4m + 5n + 2m - 3n$
   **c** $6x + 2y + 9x - 7y$      **d** $8u - 3v + 2u + 6v$
   **e** $12r - 8s + 3r + 5s$      **f** $9p - 4q + 11p + 7q$
   **g** $8m - 7n + 3m + 2n$      **h** $15y - 4z + 10y + 12z$
   **i** $11x - 4y - 10x - 5y$

**3 a** $5x + 3x^2 + 2x$    **b** $9y + 5y^2 - 4y$    **c** $10z - 3z^2 + 6z$
   **d** $10t - 4t^2 - 7t$    **e** $3u^2 + 5u + 11u^2$    **f** $10s^2 - 7s - 9s^2$

**4** Simplify each expression by division.

   **a** $\dfrac{12m}{4}$     **b** $\dfrac{18n}{9}$     **c** $\dfrac{15p}{5p}$     **d** $\dfrac{20pq}{5p}$

   **e** $\dfrac{24u^2}{8u}$     **f** $\dfrac{25u^2v}{5u}$     **g** $\dfrac{30mn^2}{6n}$     **h** $\dfrac{28u^2v}{7uv}$

   **i** $\dfrac{32pq^2}{8pq}$     **j** $\dfrac{(6r + 8)}{2}$     **k** $\dfrac{(15s + 10)}{5}$     **l** $\dfrac{(3t^2 + 2t)}{t}$

   **m** $\dfrac{(5u^2 + 3u)}{u}$     **n** $\dfrac{(7v^2 - 5v)}{v}$     **o** $\dfrac{(9u^2 - 6u)}{3u}$     **p** $\dfrac{(12x^2 - 8x)}{4x}$

**5** Copy and complete the table.

| Length (cm) | 4m | 5n | 4p | 5x | 5q | 6u |
|---|---|---|---|---|---|---|
| Width (cm) | 2m | 3n | 4p | 4x | 3r | 3v |
| Height (cm) | 3m | 3n | 4p | 2y | 2q | 2v |
| Volume (cm³) | | | | | | |

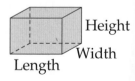

  **Algebra** Collecting like terms including powers

# 5c Expanding brackets

> **example**
>
> Expand and simplify $3(2t - 3) - 2(t + 4)$
>
> ..............................................................
>
> $3(2t - 3) - 2(t + 4) = 6t - 9 - 2t - 8 = 4t - 17$

**1** Expand these brackets.

**a** $3(2x + 4)$    **b** $2(4y - 3)$    **c** $x(x + 5)$    **d** $m(n - 7)$

**e** $u(8 - v)$    **f** $3x(x + 2)$    **g** $4x(x - y)$    **h** $-5(3p + 2)$

**i** $-6(4 - 3r)$    **j** $-5s(s - 6)$

**2** Expand and simplify these expressions.

**a** $4(2x + 3) + 5(3x + 2)$        **b** $2(3y + 4) + 3(5y - 2)$

**c** $5(6z + 3) + 4(2z - 5)$        **d** $3(t - 4) + 6(3t + 4)$

**e** $6(2k - 3) + 4(2k + 3)$        **f** $2(4u - 1) + 3(5u - 2)$

**g** $5(2r + 3) - 2(3r + 4)$        **h** $3(5s - 2) - 2(4s + 5)$

**i** $4(2m + 3) - 3(3m - 5)$        **j** $5(2p - 3) - 6(p - 4)$

**k** $7(3q - 5) - 4(3q - 5)$        **l** $6(2r - 3) - 2(1 - 3r)$

**3** Find an expression for the shaded areas.

(All dimensions are in centimetres.)

**a**
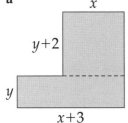

**b**
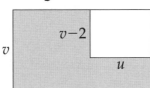

**c**
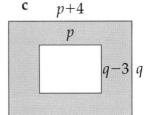

**4 a** Find an expression for the distance from Redhill to Brighton.

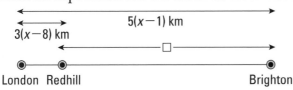

**b** Find the distance from London to each place if $x = 18$.

**Algebra** Expanding brackets    **27**

> example
>
> Factorise $2p^2 + 6pq$
>
> . . . . . . . . . . . . . . . . . . . . . . . . . . . . . . . . . . . . . . . . . . . . . . . . . . . . .
>
> $2p^2 + 6pq = 2p(p + 3q)$

For questions **1** to **3** factorise the expressions.

**1 a** $3x + 9$ **b** $7y + 21$ **c** $4z - 12$ **d** $8m - 16$
**e** $8t - 12$ **f** $14u - 49$ **g** $pq + 5p$ **h** $uv - 9v$
**i** $7yz - 3y$ **j** $9uv - 7v$

**2 a** $p^2 + 5pq$ **b** $u^2 + 9uv$ **c** $r^2 - 3rs$ **d** $x^2 - 4xy$
**e** $5m^2 - 3mn$ **f** $8u^2 - 7uv$ **g** $12r^2 - 7rs$ **h** $9p^2 - 8pq$

**3 a** $6xy + 9x$ **b** $6pq + 8q$ **c** $9uv - 6u$ **d** $15mn - 5n$
**e** $8p^2 + 12p$ **f** $21q^2 + 28q$ **g** $12r^2 - 18r$ **h** $18s^2 - 45s$
**i** $16t - 24t^2$ **j** $30u + 5u^2$

**4** Zeke knows that when his car is gathering speed his
distance after $t$ seconds is given by the expression $2t^2 + t$.
**a** Factorise this expression.
**b** Using the formula that average speed equals
distance divided by time, find an expression for
his average speed.

# 5e Formulae 1

The perimeter ($P$) of the isosceles triangle is given by the formula $P = 2a + b$.
Find $P$ if $a = 5$ and $b = 3$.

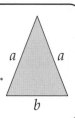

$P = 2a + b = 2 \times 5 + 3 = 13$

**1** Find the value of the required variable using each of these formulae.

**a** $P = 8d$       Find $P$ if $d = 1.5$.

**b** $A = LW$      Find $A$ if $L = 7.5$ and $W = 4$.

**c** $A = \frac{1}{2}bh$     Find $A$ if $b = 8$ and $h = 2.25$.

**d** $V = xyz$      Find $V$ if $x = 5$, $y = 3$ and $z = 1.2$.

**e** $V = p^2q$      Find $V$ if $p = 5$ and $q = 4$.

**f** $V = n^3$       Find $V$ if $n = 8$.

**g** $P = 2L + 2W$   Find $P$ if $L = 5$ and $W = 4.5$.

**h** $v = u + at$     Find $v$ if $u = 5$, $a = 10$ and $t = 2$.

**i** $P = \dfrac{mg}{A}$      Find $P$ if $m = 5$, $g = 10$ and $A = 2.5$.

**j** $k = \dfrac{RA}{d}$     Find $k$ if $R = 5$, $A = 0.01$ and $d = 2$.

**2** Zodia sees two packets of potatoes, one marked 5.5 lb and the other marked 2.4 kg and they are for sale at the same price. Use the formula given to find which is the better buy.

$$\text{Number of kg} = \frac{5}{11} \times \text{number of lb}$$

**3** If cubes are arranged in a row on a table, the number of visible faces ($N$) is given by the formula

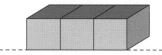

$N = 3n + 2$, where $n$ is the number of cubes. Find $N$ if $n$ equals **a** 3    **b** 5    **c** 10    **d** 20    **e** 50

The area of the shape ($A$) is given by the formula $A = ab + a^2$.
Make $b$ the subject of the formula.

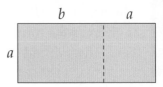

$A = ab + a^2$ therefore $A - a^2 = ab$

so $b = \dfrac{(A - a^2)}{a}$

**1** Make $x$ the subject of these formulae.

**a** $x + a = b$     **b** $x - m = n$     **c** $x + p = q + r$

**d** $x + m + n = p$     **e** $ax = b$     **f** $\dfrac{x}{u} = v$

**g** $tx = u - v$     **h** $mx - n = p$     **i** $3x - u = v$

**j** $ax + b = c$     **k** $px - q = r$     **l** $3ux - v = w$

**2** The perimeter ($P$) of the isosceles triangle is given by the formula $P = 2a + b$.

**a** Make $a$ the subject of the formula.

**b** Find $a$ if $P = 25$ and $b = 11$.

**3** The perimeter ($P$) of the isosceles trapezium is given by the formula $P = 2a + b + c$.

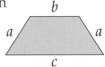

**a** Make $a$ the subject of the formula.

**b** Find $a$ if $P = 50$, $b = 10$ and $c = 16$.

**4 a** Write a formula for $D$, the distance from Newcastle to Carlisle.

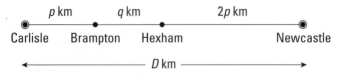

**b** Make $p$ the subject of the formula.

**c** Find $p$ if $D = 96$ and $q = 48$.

example

Find the unknown angles.

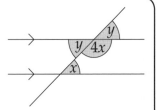

· · · · · · · · · · · · · · · · · · · · · · · · · · · · · · · · · · · · · · · ·

$x + 4x = 180°$, because allied angles are supplementary.
Therefore $5x = 180°$, so $x = 36°$, and $4x = 144°$.
$y = 36°$, because alternate, corresponding and opposite
angles are equal.

For questions **1** and **2** find the unknown angles.

**1 a**

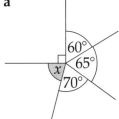

**b**

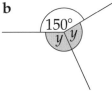

**c**

**2 a**

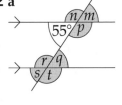

**b**

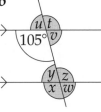

**c**

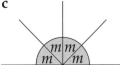

**d**

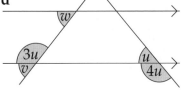

**e**

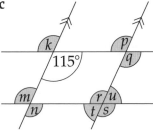

example

Find the unknown angles.

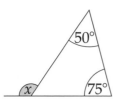

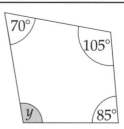

$x = 50 + 75 = 125$ degrees, because the exterior angle of a triangle equals the sum of the opposite interior pair.

$y = 360 - 70 - 105 - 85 = 100$ degrees, because the angles of a quadrilateral always total 360 degrees.

**1** Find the unknown angles.

a         b         c         d

  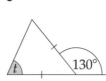 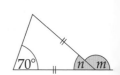

**2** Copy and complete the table for the quadrilaterals.
(Angles are measured in degrees.)

| First angle | Second angle | Third angle | Fourth angle | Are the diagonals equal in length? | Do both diagonals bisect each other? | Do the diagonals cross at Right angles? | Type of quadrilateral |
|---|---|---|---|---|---|---|---|
| 115 | 65 | 115 | | No | Yes | Yes | |
| 102 | 78 | 102 | | No | Yes | No | |
| 52 | 128 | 128 | | Yes | No | No | |
| 135 | 25 | 135 | | No | No | Yes | |

**example**

A 50p piece is a regular heptagon. Find its exterior angle.

The exterior angle $= 360 \div$ number of sides $= 360 \div 7 = 51\frac{3}{7}^{\circ}$.

**1** Copy and complete the table for the angles of these
regular polygons.

| Regular polygon | Number of sides ($n$) | Sum of angles ($S$) ($S = (n-2)180°$) | Exterior angle ($360° \div n$) | Interior angle |
|---|---|---|---|---|
| Octagon | 8 | | | |
| Decagon | 10 | | | |
| Dodecagon | 12 | | | |
| 15 sided | 15 | | | |
| 20 sided | 20 | | | |
| 24 sided | 24 | | | |

**2** The diagram shows how regular hexagons and
rhombuses can tessellate. Copy the diagram
and extend the pattern by drawing at least four
more figures of each kind.

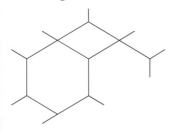

**3** Draw a diagram to show how a regular octagon can
be made by using
**a** two isosceles trapeziums and one rectangle
**b** two isosceles trapeziums and two obtuse angled
isosceles triangles.

example

Measure the side lengths of the two squares and state whether or not they are congruent.

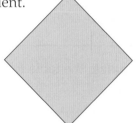

. . . . . . . . . . . . . . . . . . . . . . . . . . . . . . . . . . . . . . . . . . . . . . . . .

Both squares have a side length of 2.5 cm, therefore they are congruent.

Measure the side lengths of these figures. Find which figure **a**, **b** or **c** is not congruent to the other two.

**1 a**    **b**    **c**

**2 a**    **b**    **c**

**3 a**    **b**    **c**

**4 a**    **b**    **c**

**a** For the solid illustrated, find
  **i** the number of faces ($F$)
  **ii** the number of vertices ($V$)
  **iii** the number of edges ($E$).

**b** Check your answers using Euler's
  formula $F + V = E + 2$

............................................................

**a i** $F = 5$  **ii** $V = 6$  **iii** $E = 9$    **b** $F + V = 11$ and $E + 2 = 11$,
  therefore the answers are correct.

**1** Each of the nets below forms a solid. For each
  **a** state the mathematical name of the solid.
  **b** find the number of faces ($F$), the number
    of vertices ($V$) and the number of
    edges ($E$).
  **c** Check all your answers with the formula
    $F + V = E + 2$.

**i**              **ii**              **iii**              **iv**

**2 a** For the solid illustrated, find
  **i** the number of faces ($F$)
  **ii** the number of vertices ($V$)
  **iii** the number of edges ($E$).
  **b** Check your answers with the formula
    $F + V = E + 2$.

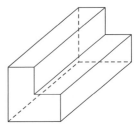

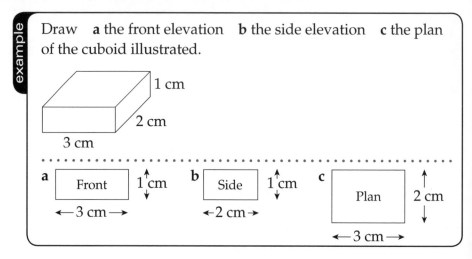

example

Draw **a** the front elevation **b** the side elevation **c** the plan of the cuboid illustrated.

**1** For each of these solids draw **i** the front elevation **ii** the side elevation **iii** the plan.

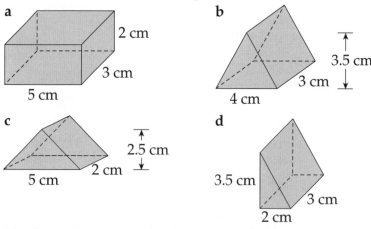

**2** The front elevation, side elevation and plan are drawn for a solid made from cubes. Make a 3-D drawing of the solid.

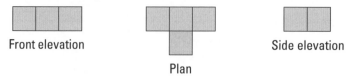

Front elevation

Plan

Side elevation

example

Solve the equation $5x - 7 = 3x + 5$

................................................................

$$5x - 7 = 3x + 5$$

Therefore $5x - 3x = 7 + 5$

Therefore $\quad\quad 2x = 12$

So $\quad\quad\quad\quad x = 6$

For questions **1** to **3** solve the equations.

**1 a** $x + 5 = 17$      **b** $y - 8 = 23$      **c** $3u + 7 = 34$
  **d** $3(v + 4) = 21$      **e** $4(w - 5) = 36$      **f** $3(4n + 5) = 27$
  **g** $24 - p = 15$      **h** $35 - q = 23$

**2 a** $3(2x + 5) + 4(3x + 1) = 109$      **b** $5(2y + 3) + 3(5y - 2) = 84$
  **c** $4(3z - 7) + 3(5z + 1) = 56$      **d** $6(3t - 2) + 4(t - 5) = 78$
  **e** $4(5u + 3) - 5(2u + 1) = 27$      **f** $2(6v - 5) - 4(2v - 7) = 26$

**3 a** $6x + 7 = 3x + 25$      **b** $7y - 3 = 2y + 17$
  **c** $8z - 35 = 2z - 5$      **d** $3(8x + 1) = 5(4x + 3)$
  **e** $3(6y - 1) = 7(2y + 3)$      **f** $5(2t - 3) = 3(3t - 2)$

**4 a** If the area of this rectangle is $35 \text{ cm}^2$, find the value of $x$.

$(2x - 1)$ cm

5 cm

  **b** If the perimeter of this rectangle is 22 cm, find the value of $y$.

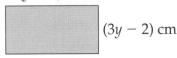

$(y + 5)$ cm

$(3y - 2)$ cm

**5** If the perimeter of this trapezium is 27 cm
  **a** find the value of $z$.
  **b** find the area of the trapezium.

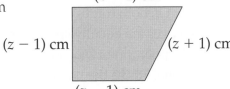

$(z + 4)$ cm

$(z - 1)$ cm            $(z + 1)$ cm

$(z - 1)$ cm

## 7b Linear equations 2

Solve the equation $3(5x - 11) = 4(6 - x)$

$$3(5x - 11) = 4(6 - x)$$

Therefore $15x - 33 = 24 - 4x$

Therefore $\qquad 19x = 57$

So $\qquad\qquad x = 3$

For questions **1** to **3** solve the equations.

**1 a** $16 - x = 9$      **b** $28 - 3y = 10$      **c** $26 - 5z = 11$
   **d** $11 - 4u = 3$      **e** $8 - v = 13$      **f** $17 - 2m = 21$
   **g** $5 - 6n = 23$      **h** $12 - 7p = 82$

**2 a** $2x + 12 = 27 - 3x$      **b** $4y + 5 = 50 - 5y$
   **c** $5z + 18 = 108 - 10z$      **d** $9u - 56 = 24 - 7u$
   **e** $17v - 15 = 60 - 8v$      **f** $12m - 21 = 35 - 16m$

**3 a** $2(x + 2) = 5(11 - 3x)$      **b** $3(3y + 1) = 7(13 - 5y)$
   **c** $3(2z + 3) = 5(8 - 5z)$      **d** $5(5u - 3) = 7(9 - 2u)$
   **e** $2(4v - 5) = 7(11 - 3v)$      **f** $4(2p - 7) = 5(10 - p)$

**4** The two rectangles illustrated have the same area. Find **a** the value of $x$ **b** the common area.

$(9 - x)$ cm

$(3x + 1)$ cm

3 cm

5 cm

**5** The distance between Westville and Eastville is the same by either of the two motorways shown. On both routes the services are equally spaced, they are $40 + d$ km apart on the upper motorway and $37 - d$ km apart on the lower one. Find **a** the value of $d$ **b** the distance between Westville and Eastville by either route.

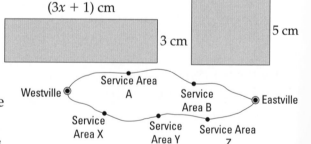

Westville   Service Area A   Service Area B   Eastville

Service Area X   Service Area Y   Service Area Z

**a** Draw a mapping for $x \longrightarrow 2x - 1$ using values of $x$ from 1 to 3.

**b** Find the inverse for this function.

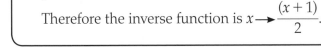

**a**

Input, $x$

Output, $y$

..............................

**b** The function rule is 'Multiply by 2 and then subtract 1'. The reverse procedure is 'Add one and then divide the result by 2'.

Therefore the inverse function is $x \longrightarrow \dfrac{(x + 1)}{2}$.

**1** For each function, copy and complete this table of values.

| $x =$ | 1 | 2 | 3 | 4 | 5 |
|-------|---|---|---|---|---|
| $y =$ |   |   |   |   |   |

**a** $y = 4x$    **b** $y = 2x + 1$    **c** $y = 2(x - 1)$

**d** $y = 6 - x$    **e** $x + y = 8$

**2** Copy and complete this mapping diagram for $x \longrightarrow 10 - 2x$. Use values of $x$ from 0 to 5.

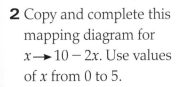

Input, $x$

Output, $y$

**3** Copy and complete this mapping diagram for $x \longrightarrow \dfrac{(10 - x)}{2}$. Use even values of $x$ from 0 to 10. Comparing your diagram with that for question **2**, what do you notice? What is the connection between the two functions?

Input, $x$

Output, $y$

**4** Find the inverse of each of these functions.

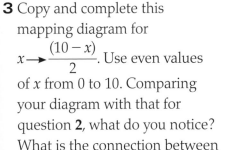

**a** $x \longrightarrow 5x$    **b** $x \longrightarrow x + 8$    **c** $x \longrightarrow 2x + 3$

**d** $x \longrightarrow 5x - 2$    **e** $x \longrightarrow 2(x - 3)$    **f** $x \longrightarrow \dfrac{(x + 3)}{2}$

**example**

**a** Copy and complete the table for the function $y = 2x - 3$.

| $x =$ | 0 | 1 | 2 | 3 |
|---|---|---|---|---|
| $y =$ | | | | |

**b** Plot the points on a grid and join them with a straight line.

**c** Give the coordinates for the intersection point of the line with **i** the $x$ axis **ii** the $y$ axis.

**b**

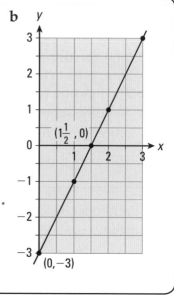

· · · · · · · · · · · · · · · · · · · · · · · · · · · · · · · · · · · · · · · · ·

**a**

| $x =$ | 0 | 1 | 2 | 3 |
|---|---|---|---|---|
| $y =$ | -3 | -1 | 1 | 3 |

**c i** $(1\frac{1}{2}, 0)$      **ii** $(0, -3)$

For questions **1** and **2**, draw a grid with both axes labelled from -5 to 12.

**1 a** Copy and complete the table for the functions
    **i** $y = 2x$    **ii** $y = x - 1$    **iii** $y = 9 - x$

| $x =$ | -2 | 2 | 6 |
|---|---|---|---|
| $y =$ | | | |

   **b** Plot each set of points on the same grid and join each set with a straight line.

   **c** For each line give the coordinates for the intersection point with **i** the $x$ axis **ii** the $y$ axis.

   **d** Give the coordinates of the three points where the graph lines intersect.

**2 a** Copy and complete the table for the functions
    **i** $y = x + 3$     **ii** $y = 5 + x$    **iii** $y = -1$

| $x =$ | -5 | 2 | 8 |
|---|---|---|---|
| $y =$ | | | |

   **b** Plot each set of points on the same grid and join each set with a straight line.

   **c** Give the coordinates of the three points where the graph lines intersect.

**example**

The function $y = \frac{1}{2}x + 1$ is plotted on a graph.
Find **a** the gradient
**b** the $y$ intercept.

. . . . . . . . . . . . . . . . . . . . . . . . . . . . . .

**a** The gradient is $\frac{1}{2}$.
(the coefficient of $x$)
**b** The $y$ intercept is at $y = 1$.
(the constant term)

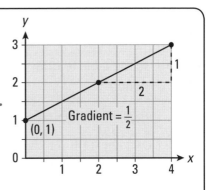

**1** Copy the grid illustrated.

**a** Mr. Sparky is an electrician and the table shows his repair charges paid by three people.

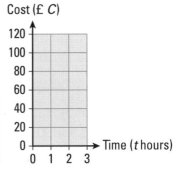

|  | Time for the repair ($t$) | Cost ($C$) |
|---|---|---|
| Zodia | 1 h | £80 |
| Zeke | 2 h | £100 |
| Marcus | 3 h | £120 |

Plot these details on the graph grid and find
**i** the gradient (his charge per hour)
**ii** the $C$ intercept (his call-out charge)
**iii** the equation of the line.

**b** Mr. Cirky is also an electrician but his charges are given by the equation $C = 20 + 40t$. Draw the line for his equation on your grid also.

**c** Cam needs a repair doing that will take $1\frac{1}{2}$ hours. Who will do it cheaper and by how much?

**d** Sia needs a repair doing that will take $2\frac{1}{2}$ h. Who will do it cheaper and by how much?

# 7e² Curved graphs

**a** Copy and complete the table for the function $y = x^2 + 1$.

**b** Use the table to draw a graph of the function.

| $x =$ | -2 | -1 | 0 | 1 | 2 |
|---|---|---|---|---|---|
| $x^2 =$ | | | | | |
| $+1 =$ | | | | | |
| $y =$ | | | | | |

. . . . . . . . . . . . . . . . . . . . . . . . . . . . . . . . . . . . . . . . . . . . . . . . . . . .

**a**

| $x =$ | -2 | -1 | 0 | 1 | 2 |
|---|---|---|---|---|---|
| $x^2 =$ | 4 | 1 | 0 | 1 | 4 |
| $+1 =$ | 1 | 1 | 1 | 1 | 1 |
| $y =$ | 5 | 2 | 1 | 2 | 5 |

**b**

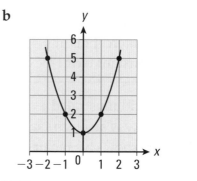

Make a copy of the table and the grid for questions **1** and **2**.

**1** Complete the table for the function $y = x^2 - 2$.

| $x =$ | -3 | -2 | -1 | 0 | 1 | 2 | 3 |
|---|---|---|---|---|---|---|---|
| $x^2 =$ | | | | | | | |
| $-2 =$ | | | | | | | |
| $y =$ | | | | | | | |

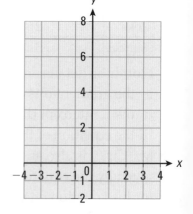

**2** Use your completed table to draw a graph of the function. (Join the points with a smooth curve.)

**3** Give the coordinates of the point where the graph cuts the $y$ axis.

**4** Give the coordinates of the minimum point on the curve.

example

Let A and B be the end points of a line segment and M be its midpoint.

**a** Given A (-2, 2) and B(4, -3), find M.

**b** Given A (1, 2) and M (3, 3), find B.

**a** $M = \left(\frac{-2+4}{2}, \frac{2-3}{2}\right) = \left(\frac{2}{2}, \frac{-1}{2}\right) = (1, -0.5)$

**b** Let B = $(x, y)$ then

$$\frac{1+x}{2} = 3 \qquad \frac{2+y}{2} = 3$$

$$1 + x = 6 \qquad 2 + y = 6$$

$$x = 5 \qquad y = 4$$

$$B = (5, 4)$$

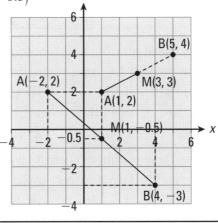

**1** Find the midpoints of these pairs of points.

  **a** (2, 0) and (6, 4)   **b** (3, -3) and (3, -5)

  **c** (4, 6) and (-4, 3)   **d** (-8, -5) and (-2, -1)

**2** A line segment AB has midpoint M. Given A and M, find the coordinates of B.

  **a** A (1, 1) and M (2, 3)   **b** A (-2, 1) and M (4, 3)

  **c** A (2, 2) and M (-2, 3)   **d** A (-3, -2) and M (-4, -2)

**3** A (-3, -1), B (3, 1), C (5, 7) and D form a rhombus.

  **a** Find the coordinates of D.

  **b** Calculate the coordinates of the midpoints of each side, $M_{AB}$, $M_{BC}$, $M_{CD}$ and $M_{DA}$.

  **c** Find P the midpoint of $M_{AB}$ and $M_{CD}$ and Q the midpoint of $M_{BC}$ and $M_{DA}$. Comment on what you find.

**example**

**a** Express 2752 to the nearest hundred.

**b** Express 1.253 to 2 dp.

. . . . . . . . . . . . . . . . . . . . . . . . . . . . . . . . . . . . . . . . . . . .

**a** 27<u>5</u>2 = 2800 to the nearest hundred, because if the tens figure is 5 or greater the hundreds figure must be rounded up.

**b** 1.25<u>3</u> = 1.25 to 2 dp, because the third decimal place figure is less than 5, so it is neglected.

**1** Give these numbers correct to **a** the nearest 1000
**b** the nearest 100 **c** the nearest 10.

| | | | |
|---|---|---|---|
| **i** 18 784 | **ii** 23 276 | **iii** 11 932 | **iv** 13 193 |
| **v** 8268 | **vi** 6481 | **vii** 3319 | **viii** 7654 |
| **ix** 942 | **x** 826 | **xi** 631 | **xii** 992 |

**2** Give these numbers correct to **a** the nearest whole number
**b** correct to 1 dp **c** correct to 2 dp **d** correct to 3 dp.

| | | | |
|---|---|---|---|
| **i** 5.8632 | **ii** 7.9764 | **iii** 3.2946 | **iv** 8.7348 |
| **v** 6.1499 | **vi** 4.3851 | **vii** 9.9834 | **viii** 15.6294 |
| **ix** 0.843 73 | **x** 0.982 61 | **xi** 0.710 48 | **xii** 0.990 97 |

**3** The area of the rectangle is worked
out to the nearest whole number.
Is the answer 70 cm² or 71 cm²?

7.2 cm

9.8 cm

**4** Ronnie is doing a physics experiment to
find the power in watts of a small light bulb.
He has to use the formula

Power (watts) = Voltage (volts) × Current (amps)

His voltmeter reads 3.2 volts and his ammeter
reads 0.75 amps. Is the power of his bulb 2 or 3 watts
when expressed to the nearest whole number?

**5** Eshe rides her bike between two lamp posts which are
12.6 m apart in 3.6 seconds. When expressed to the nearest
whole number is her speed 3 m per second or 4 m per second?

> **example**
>
> **a** Calculate $3.7 + 6.9$ by using a partition method.
> **b** Calculate $5.1 - 0.95$ by using a compensation method.
> ...........................................................................
> **a** $3.7 + 6.9 = 3.7 + 6 + 0.9 = 9.7 + 0.9 = 10.6$
> **b** $5.1 - 0.95 = 5.1 - 1 + 0.05 = 4.1 + 0.05 = 4.15$

**1** Calculate these expressions using the partition method.

  **a** $8.7 + 6.6$     **b** $9.2 + 7.9$     **c** $6.5 + 4.8$     **d** $10.2 + 9.7$

  **e** $11.5 + 12.3$   **f** $13.6 + 11.5$   **g** $15.2 + 13.4$   **h** $16.7 + 10.9$

**2** Calculate these expressions using the compensation method.

  **a** $8.52 - 2.98$     **b** $6.83 - 3.99$     **c** $9.15 - 4.96$

  **d** $9.33 - 3.01$     **e** $10.38 - 5.05$    **f** $12.59 - 7.06$

  **g** $2.83 + 1.98$     **h** $4.32 + 3.95$     **i** $5.99 + 4.99$

  **j** $5.22 + 3.07$     **k** $8.39 + 1.03$     **l** $7.48 + 2.05$

**3** Using any convenient method, find which part – **i**, **ii** or **iii** – has a different answer from the other two.

  **a i** $365.24 + 125.3 + 412$     **b i** $91.56 + 25 + 15.84$
    **ii** $672 + 99.63 + 131.91$       **ii** $101.12 + 11.6 + 19.58$
    **iii** $98.15 + 508.02 + 296.37$    **iii** $52.13 + 36.95 + 43.22$

  **c i** $317.52 - 221.34$       **d i** $97.3 - 43.72$
    **ii** $125.29 - 28.11$        **ii** $105.18 - 51.5$
    **iii** $150.3 - 54.12$       **iii** $120 - 66.42$

**4** Tom walks 1.4 km from his house to Jane's house. How long is Larch Avenue?

**5 a** The times for the four runners in a 4 by 200 m relay race were 30.65 s, 31.30 s, 32.15 s and 31.85 s. Find their total time.

  **b** The time for this event broke the school's record which had stood at 126.10 s. By how much did they better the record?

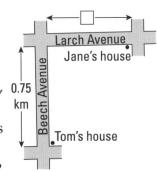

example

Calculate **a** $0.32 \div 0.01$ **b** $57.2 \times 10^3$

. . . . . . . . . . . . . . . . . . . . . . . . . . . . . . . . . . . . . . . . . . . . .

**a** $0.32 \div 0.01 = 32$ (Dividing by $1/100$ is the same as multiplying by 100.)

**b** $57.2 \times 10^3 = 57\ 200$ (The decimal point is moved three places to the right.)

**1 a** Multiply these by 0.1. **i** 264 **ii** 95 **iii** 8 **iv** 56.2 **v** 9.7
  **vi** 6.53 **vii** 0.8 **viii** 0.16 **ix** 0.051 **x** 0.0076

 **b** Multiply these by 0.01. **i** 532 **ii** 81 **iii** 3 **iv** 37.6 **v** 8.2
  **vi** 3.57 **vii** 0.5 **viii** 0.73 **ix** 0.084 **x** 0.0086

 **c** Divide these by 0.1. **i** 633 **ii** 83 **iii** 5 **iv** 71.6 **v** 4.3
  **vi** 9.13 **vii** 0.3 **viii** 0.51 **ix** 0.028 **x** 0.0039

 **d** Divide these by 0.01. **i** 824 **ii** 87 **iii** 2 **iv** 64.9 **v** 6.8
  **vi** 7.25 **vii** 0.2 **viii** 0.43 **ix** 0.055 **x** 0.0031

**2 a** Multiply these by $10^2$. **i** 56 **ii** 7 **iii** 8.3 **iv** 9.25
  **v** 0.6 **vi** 0.35

 **b** Multiply these by $10^3$. **i** 8 **ii** 2.5 **iii** 7.63 **iv** 0.9
  **v** 0.72 **vi** 0.04

 **c** Divide these by $10^2$. **i** 391 **ii** 67 **iii** 48.3 **iv** 7.5
  **v** 3.61 **vi** 0.54

 **d** Divide these by $10^3$. **i** 1325 **ii** 415 **iii** 94 **iv** 52.3
  **v** 9.46 **vi** 0.51

**3 a** Multiply these by $10^{-1}$. **i** 183 **ii** 37 **iii** 7 **iv** 78.5 **v** 4.1
  **vi** 7.82 **vii** 0.7 **viii** 0.53 **ix** 0.068 **x** 0.0028

 **b** Multiply these by $10^{-2}$. **i** 465 **ii** 59 **iii** 6 **iv** 91.2 **v** 4.8
  **vi** 8.03 **vii** 0.9 **viii** 0.67 **ix** 0.029 **x** 0.0031

 **c** Divide these by $10^{-1}$. **i** 612 **ii** 65 **iii** 9 **iv** 33.4 **v** 5.2
  **vi** 6.52 **vii** 0.6 **viii** 0.27 **ix** 0.015 **x** 0.0045

 **d** Divide these by $10^{-2}$. **i** 625 **ii** 32 **iii** 4 **iv** 81.2 **v** 4.3
  **vi** 8.43 **vii** 0.4 **viii** 0.62 **ix** 0.081 **x** 0.0012

# 8d Multiplication

example

**a** Use the factor method to calculate $3.1 \times 15$.
**b** Use the partition method to calculate $5.3 \times 23$.

· · · · · · · · · · · · · · · · · · · · · · · · · · · · · · · · · · · · · · · · · · · · · · · · · · ·

**a** $3.1 \times 15 = 3.1 \times 5 \times 3 = 15.5 \times 3 = 46.5$
**b** $5.3 \times 23 = (5.3 \times 20) + (5.3 \times 3) = 106 + 15.9 = 121.9$

**1 a** Use the factor method to calculate
   **i** $47 \times 35$    **ii** $92 \times 36$    **iii** $104 \times 21$
   **iv** $136 \times 45$    **v** $205 \times 42$

  **b** Use the partition method to calculate
   **i** $64 \times 31$    **ii** $56 \times 23$    **iii** $81 \times 52$
   **iv** $125 \times 24$    **v** $135 \times 16$

**2 a** Use the factor method to calculate
   **i** $6.3 \times 21$    **ii** $9.2 \times 25$    **iii** $8.4 \times 15$    **iv** $10.2 \times 35$
   **v** $21.5 \times 42$    **vi** $75 \times 0.02$    **vii** $45 \times 0.05$    **viii** $29 \times 0.08$

  **b** Use the partition method to calculate
   **i** $7.5 \times 21$    **ii** $8.6 \times 32$    **iii** $10.8 \times 25$

**3** Using any convenient method, find which part – **i**, **ii** or
**iii** – has a different answer from the other two.
  **a i** $36 \times 5.4$    **ii** $159.5 \times 1.2$    **iii** $24 \times 8.1$
  **b i** $63 \times 0.48$    **ii** $121 \times 0.25$    **iii** $36 \times 0.84$
  **c i** $40.5 \times 0.28$    **ii** $126 \times 0.09$    **iii** $20.6 \times 0.55$
  **d i** $55.8 \times 1.4$    **ii** $50.08 \times 1.5$    **iii** $15.65 \times 4.8$

**4** Eight people were waiting at a bus stop, but by the time
the bus arrived there were 2.25 times as many. How many
people boarded the bus if no one stayed behind?

**5 a** When Kanika started school she was 120 cm tall. If she
is now 1.35 times taller, how tall is she now?
  **b** When Josiah started school his mass was 24 kg. If he is
now 2.375 times heavier, what is his mass now?

example

> **a** Use the factor method to calculate $444 \div 12$.
> **b** Use the partition method to calculate $832 \div 16$
> ● ● ● ● ● ● ● ● ● ● ● ● ● ● ● ● ● ● ● ● ● ● ● ● ● ● ● ● ● ● ● ● ● ● ● ● ● ● ● ● ● ● ● ● ●
> **a** $444 \div 12 = 444 \div 4 \div 3 = 111 \div 3 = 37$
> **b** $832 \div 16 = (800 \div 16) + (32 \div 16) = 50 + 2 = 52$

**1** Use the factor method to calculate

    **a** $768 \div 12$     **b** $990 \div 18$     **c** $504 \div 14$     **d** $720 \div 16$

    **e** $924 \div 21$     **f** $1320 \div 24$     **g** $1176 \div 28$     **h** $1300 \div 25$

**2** Use the partition method to calculate

    **a** $630 \div 15$     **b** $954 \div 18$     **c** $896 \div 16$     **d** $475 \div 25$

    **e** $770 \div 35$     **f** $948 \div 12$     **g** $756 \div 14$     **h** $1550 \div 25$

    **i** $1896 \div 24$     **j** $1584 \div 12$

**3** Using any convenient method, find which part – **i**, **ii** or **iii** – has a different answer from the other two.

    **a i** $43.2 \div 6$     **ii** $52.5 \div 7$     **iii** $64.8 \div 9$

    **b i** $56.7 \div 27$     **ii** $31.5 \div 15$     **iii** $38.4 \div 16$

    **c i** $7.36 \div 16$     **ii** $11.25 \div 25$     **iii** $6.75 \div 15$

    **d i** $328.8 \div 16$     **ii** $364.5 \div 18$     **iii** $445.5 \div 22$

**4** Using any convenient method, find which part – **i**, **ii** or **iii** – has a different answer from the other two.

    **a i** $156 \div 2.5$     **ii** $225 \div 3.6$     **iii** $175 \div 2.8$

    **b i** $144 \div 6.4$     **ii** $81 \div 3.6$     **iii** $99 \div 4.5$

    **c i** $112 \div 3.5$     **ii** $56 \div 1.6$     **iii** $48 \div 1.5$

    **d i** $7 \div 5.6$     **ii** $9 \div 7.5$     **iii** $8 \div 6.4$

**5** An electrician has a cable that is $40.5\,m$ long. If he cuts it into 9 equal parts, how long will each part be?

Use your calculator to find
**a** $\sqrt{5}$    **b** $\sqrt[3]{4}$
Give your answers to 1 dp.

**a** $\sqrt{5} = 2.2\underline{3}.... = 2.2$ to 1 dp
**b** $\sqrt[3]{4} = 1.5\underline{8}.... = 1.6$ to 1 dp

**1 a** Use your calculator to find the square root of each of these
numbers correct to 1 dp.
   **i** 90　　　　**ii** 30　　　　**iii** 500　　　　**iv** 2000

**b** Use your calculator to find the cube root of each of these
numbers correct to 1 dp.
   **i** 50　　　　**ii** 90　　　　**iii** 900　　　　**iv** 600

**2 a** Use the trial-and-improvement method to find the
square root of each of these numbers to 2 dp.
   **i** 80　　　**ii** 110　　　**iii** 160
   **iv** 250　　**v** 750　　　**vi** 12

**b** Use the trial-and-improvement method to find the
cube root of each of these numbers to 2 dp.
   **i** 180　　　**ii** 580　　　**iii** 60
   **iv** 20　　　**v** 35　　　**vi** 12

**3 a** A freight container, used on lorries, trains
and ships is of cubic shape and has
volume 30 m³. Find its side length to 1 dp.

**b** A dice has a volume of 1400 mm³.
Find its side length to 1 dp.

 Volume = 1400 mm³

Volume = 30 m³

**c** An oil storage tank is of cubic shape
and has a capacity of 600 litres. Find
   **i** its volume in m³
   **ii** its side length correct to 1 dp.

Capacity = 600 litres

The square has the same area as the rectangle. Find the side length of the square to 1 dp.

15 cm × 9 cm

........................

The area of the rectangle is
$15 \times 9 = 135\,\text{cm}^2$
Therefore the side length of the square is
$\sqrt{135} = 11.6\underline{1}.... = 11.6\,\text{cm}$ to 1 dp

**1** The diagram shows a cul-de-sac road and the square at its end has the same area as the rectangular road. Find the side length of the square end correct to 1 dp.

8 m — 90 m

**2** The playground at Afiya's school is shown in the diagram. The rectangle whose dimensions are given has the same area as the square. Find the distances $x$, $y$ and $z$.

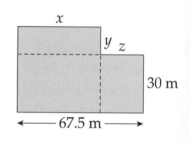

$x$ — $y$ $z$ — 30 m — 67.5 m

**3** Copy and complete the table.

| Number | 0.04 | 0.0625 | 0.16 | 0.25 | 0.36 | 0.5625 | 1 | 2.25 | 4 | 6.25 | 9 |
|---|---|---|---|---|---|---|---|---|---|---|---|
| Square root | | | | | | | | | | | |

Use your completed table to state the condition for
**a** the square root being smaller than the number
**b** the square root being larger than the number.

Change 1.05 kg to pounds (lb) and ounces (oz).
(1 oz ≈ 30 g; 1 lb = 16 oz)

. . . . . . . . . . . . . . . . . . . . . . . . . . . . . . . . . . . . . . . . . . . . . . . .

1.05 kg = 1050 g = 1050 ÷ 30 = 35 oz
35 ÷ 16 = 2 remainder 3, therefore 1.05 kg = 2 lb 3 oz.

**1** Convert these metric measurements to the units
indicated in brackets.

  **a** 435 cm (m and cm)       **b** 516 mm (cm and mm)

  **c** 2 521 326 cm (km, m and cm)   **d** 29 415 ml (litres and ml)

  **e** 31 250 g (kg and g)       **f** 18 755 240 g (t, kg and g)

  **g** 125 000 cm$^2$ (m$^2$)        **h** 5480 mm$^2$ (cm$^2$)

  **i** 1.9 m$^2$ (cm$^2$)           **j** 1.5 kg (lb and oz)

  **k** 6.25 m (feet and inches)

  (For part **k** assume that 1 m is approximately 3 feet.)

**2** Convert these time measurements into the units
indicated in the brackets.

  **a** 7530 s (hours, minutes and seconds)

  **b** 1590 min (days, hours and minutes)

  **c** 51 days (weeks and days)

  **d** 750 days (years and days)

**3** Suzanne has a 12 m length of tape and she wants to
cut it into equal lengths of 250 cm. How many lengths
will she make and what length will be left over?

**4** There are 522 people on a cross channel ferry and all of
them have ordered lunch. If the restaurant on board has
180 seats how many sittings will be required? How many
people will there be at the last sitting if the others are full?

**5** A garden centre has 570 kg of compost left in stock and
the manager shares it out between 24 regular customers.
How much will each customer receive? Express your
answer in both fraction and decimal form.

Calculate $\sqrt{5^2 + 12^2} \times 5$

$\sqrt{5^2 + 12^2} \times 5 = \sqrt{25 + 144} \times 5 = \sqrt{169} \times 5 = 13 \times 5 = 65.$
(Note carefully the order of operations.)

For questions **1** to **4**, calculate the answer to each part.

**1 a** $5 + 4 \times 3$      **b** $15 - 3 \times 2$
  **c** $(15 - 3) \times 7$      **d** $(9 + 13) \div 11$
  **e** $7 \times (5 + 4) \times 3$      **f** $9 \times (18 - 12) \times 4$
  **g** $(8 + 12) \times (15 - 9)$      **h** $(20 + 25) \div (24 - 9)$

**2 a** $(5^2 + 4^2) \times 6$      **b** $(3^2 + 4^2) \div 5$

  **c** $(4^2 - 3^2) \times (5^2 - 4^2)$      **d** $\dfrac{(13^2 - 5^2)}{(10^2 - 8^2)}$

**3 a** $\sqrt{4^2 + 3^2} \times 9$      **b** $\dfrac{54}{\sqrt{15^2 - 12^2}}$

  **c** $\dfrac{\sqrt{17^2 - 8^2}}{\sqrt{8^2 + 6^2}}$      **d** $\sqrt{12^2 + 16^2} \times \sqrt{37^2 - 12^2}$

**4 a** $\dfrac{7 \times \sqrt{53^2 - 28^2}}{9}$      **b** $9 \times \sqrt{37^2 - 35^2} \div \sqrt{5^2 - 3^2}$
  **c** $960 \div 4 \times \sqrt{61^2 - 11^2}$      **d** $117 \div 6 \times \sqrt{5^2 + 12^2}$

**5** Find the area of **a** the rectangle     **b** the triangle.

**a**

50 mm

$\sqrt{(40^2 + 9^2)}$ mm

**b**

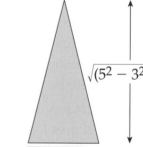

$\sqrt{(5^2 - 3^2)}$ cm

$\sqrt{(5^2 - 4^2)}$ cm

example

Rotate the triangle through 90° anticlockwise about (0,0).

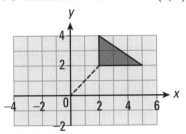

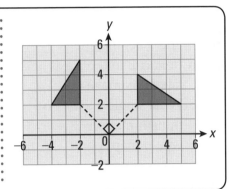

**1 a** Give the transformation that maps the shaded shape onto
  **i** A  **ii** B  **iii** C
  **iv** D  **v** E.

**b** Give also the transformation that maps
  **i** D onto E
  **ii** E onto D
  **iii** A onto E
  **iv** A onto D
  **v** B onto C.

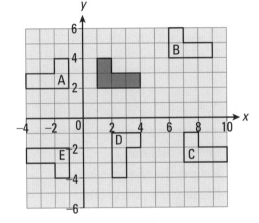

**2** Copy the diagram.

**a** Draw a rotation of the rhombus through 90° about (0,0) (in either direction) onto your copy.

**b** Your pattern should have an octagon around its centre. Is this octagon a regular one? If not, why not?

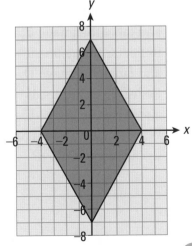

**a** Reflect triangle A in the $y$ axis and label the image B.

**b** Reflect B in the $x$ axis and label the image C.

**c** What single transformation would map A onto C?

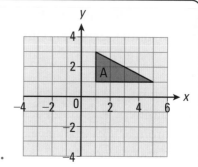

· · · · · · · · · · · · · · · · · · · · · · · · · · · ·

**a** and **b** are shown on the diagram.

**c** A rotation of 180° about $(0,0)$.

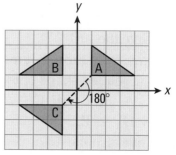

**1** Copy the diagram.

**a** Reflect the triangle A in the line $y = x$ and label the image B.

**b** Reflect B in the $y$ axis and label the image C.

**c** Reflect C in the line $y = -x$ and label the image D.

**d** Reflect D in the $x$ axis and label the image E.

**e** What single transformation would map A onto E?

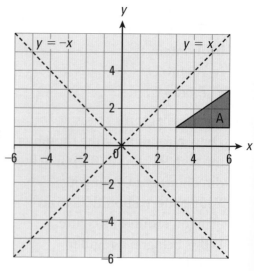

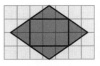
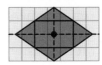

**example**

Look at the shape illustrated. Mark on it all the lines of symmetry that it has and state its order of rotational symmetry.

· · · · · · · · · · · · · · · · · · · · · · · · · · · · · · · · · · · · · · · · · · · · · · · · · · · · · · ·

The lines of symmetry are shown. Its rotational symmetry is of order 2, because if it is rotated through 180° (that is 360° divided by 2) it maps onto itself.

**1** Copy these shapes. For each shape
  **a** Draw all the lines of symmetry that the shape has onto your copy.
  **b** State the order of rotational symmetry for each shape.

**a**     **b**     **c**

**d**     **e**     **f**

**2** Copy and complete the table for quadrilaterals.

| Quadri-lateral | Square | Rec-tangle | Rhombus | Parallelo-gram | Isosceles trapezium | Kite | Arrow-head |
|---|---|---|---|---|---|---|---|
| **Number of lines of symmetry** | | | | | | | |
| **Order of rotational symmetry** | | | | | | | |

For all quadrilaterals that have a line or lines of symmetry draw a diagram which shows them clearly.

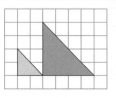

> **example**
>
> On the diagram it can be seen that the larger triangle is an enlargement of the smaller one. Give the scale factor of the enlargement and locate the position of the centre of enlargement.
>
> ...........................................................
>
> It can easily be seen that the scale factor is 2. The centre of enlargement (C) is marked with a dot.

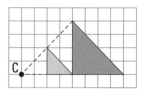

**1** Copy these diagrams. On your copies, draw the image formed by the enlargement.

**a**

Scale factor 2

**b**

Scale factor 3

**c**

Scale factor 4

**d**

Scale factor 3

**e**

Scale factor 4

**f**

Scale factor 3

**2** Layla has a set of four coffee tables that are all of the same shape but different sizes. The dimensions of the smallest one are shown in the diagram.
Find the dimensions of the other three tables if they are enlargements of the smallest one by scale factors of 2, 3 and 4.

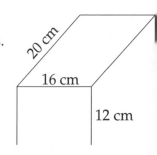

20 cm
16 cm
12 cm

example

Find the image of the square when it is enlarged by a scale factor of $\frac{1}{2}$, with the dot indicating the centre of enlargement.

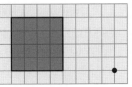

Scale factor $\frac{1}{2}$

It can be seen that an enlargement with a scale factor of $\frac{1}{2}$ is the same as a reduction by a factor of 2.

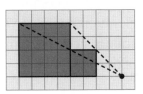

**1** Copy these diagrams. On your copies, draw the image formed by the enlargement.

**a**

Scale factor $\frac{1}{3}$

**b**

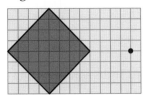

Scale factor $\frac{1}{2}$

**c**

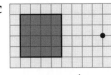

Scale factor $\frac{1}{2}$

**d**

Scale factor $\frac{1}{3}$

**e**

Scale factor $\frac{1}{4}$

**f**

Scale factor $\frac{1}{3}$

**2** Find the new side lengths if the triangle is enlarged by a scale factor of **a** $\frac{1}{3}$ **b** $\frac{1}{4}$.

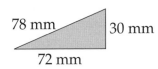

78 mm     30 mm

72 mm

> The distance between Jamal's house and his school is 25 cm on a street plan. If the scale of the plan is 1 cm to 40 m (or 1:4000), what is the real distance?
>
> ⋯⋯⋯⋯⋯⋯⋯⋯⋯⋯⋯⋯⋯⋯⋯⋯⋯⋯⋯⋯⋯⋯⋯⋯⋯
>
> The real distance is $25 \times 40 = 1000$ m.

**1** The drawings show the front elevation, side elevation and plan view of a table. If the scale is 1 cm to 75 cm, find the dimensions of the real table.

**2** The scale of a map is 1 cm to 0.2 km or 1:20 000. Copy and complete the table.

| Distance on map (cm) | 2 | 5 | | | | 15 | 17.5 | | | 25 | 27.5 |
|---|---|---|---|---|---|---|---|---|---|---|---|
| Real distance (m) | | | | | | | | | | | |
| Real distance (km) | 0.4 | | 1.5 | 2.1 | 2.5 | | | 4 | 4.5 | | |

**3** Network Rail's standard track gauge is 144 cm.
Find the track gauge of
   **a** the Romney Marsh miniature railway if its scale is 1:4 to that of Network Rail's
   **b** Jamie's model railway if its scale is 1:80 to that of Network Rail's.

**4** Suzanne has a pair of large set squares. Find the length of the longest side of each one by drawing scale diagrams.
Use a scale of 1 cm to 5 cm.

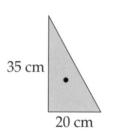

35 cm

20 cm

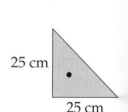

25 cm

25 cm

example

**a** State the term-to-term rule for the sequence 4, 9, 14, 19, ...

**b** Is $5n - 1$ the position-to-term rule for this sequence?

· · · · · · · · · · · · · · · · · · · · · · · · · · · · · · · · · · · · · · · · · · · · · · · ·

**a** Add 5 to the previous term.

**b** Yes, because $5 \times 1 - 1 = 4$, $5 \times 2 - 1 = 9$, $5 \times 3 - 1 = 14$ and
$5 \times 4 - 1 = 19$.

**1** Continue each of these sequences for three more terms.

   **a** 3, 5, 7, 9, ...      **b** 50, 45, 40, 35, ...      **c** 2, 6, 18, 54, ...

   **d** 1, 4, 16, 64, ...    **e** 1215, 405, 135, 45, ...   **f** $1\frac{1}{2}$, 3, $4\frac{1}{2}$, 6, ...

**2** Generate the first five terms of these sequences.

| First term | Term-to-term rule | First term | Term-to-term rule |
| --- | --- | --- | --- |
| **a** 5 | Add 3 to the previous term | **b** 3 | Add 4 to the previous term |
| **c** 45 | Subtract 6 from the previous term | **d** 42 | Subtract 5 from the previous term |
| **e** 3 | Multiply the previous term by 4 | **f** 5 | Multiply the previous term by 3 |
| **g** 5000 | Divide the previous term by 5 | **h** 64 000 | Divide the previous term by 4 |

**3** Generate the first five terms of these sequences. The
position-to-term rule is given for each one.

   **a** Multiply the position number by 4 and then add 3
      $(4n + 3)$

   **b** Multiply the position number by 3 and then subtract 1
      $(3n - 1)$

   **c** Multiply the position number by 3 and subtract
      the result from 20 $(20 - 3n)$

   **d** Divide the position number by 2 $\left(\frac{1}{2}n\right)$

   **e** Divide the position number by 2 and then add 2 $\left(\frac{1}{2}n + 2\right)$

## 10b Sequences in context

**example**

Find the $n^{\text{th}}$ term of the sequence -6, -2, 2, 6, 10, ...

· · · · · · · · · · · · · · · · · · · · · · · · · · · · · · · · · · · · · · · · · · · · · · · · · · · ·

The term-to-term rule is add 4. If there was a zeroth term it would be 4 less than -6, or -10. The $n^{\text{th}}$ term (or position-to-term rule) is therefore $4n - 10$.

**1** Find the $n^{\text{th}}$ term for each of these sequences.

  **a** 10, 13, 16, 19, 22, ...     **b** 9, 14, 19, 24, 29, ...

  **c** $4\frac{1}{2}, 5, 5\frac{1}{2}, 6, 6\frac{1}{2}, ...$     **d** 5, 12, 19, 26, 33, ...

  **e** $\frac{1}{2}, 2, 3\frac{1}{2}, 5, 6\frac{1}{2}, ...$     **f** 22, 19, 16, 13, 10, ...

**2** Find the $n^{\text{th}}$ term for each of these sequences.

  **a** -5, -2, 1, 4, 7, ...     **b** -5, -1, 3, 7, 11, ...

  **c** -4, 2, 8, 14, 20, ...     **d** 5, 2, -1, -4, -7, ...

  **e** 7, 2, -3, -8, -13, ...     **f** 5, 1, -3, -7, -11, ...

**3** Look at the diagram.
Copy and complete the table.

$n$   =   1       2       3

| Term number | 1 | 2 | 3 | 4 | 5 | ... | $n$ |
|---|---|---|---|---|---|---|---|
| Number of shaded squares | | | | | | | |

**4** Look at the diagram.
Copy and complete the table.

$n$   =   1       2       3

| Term number | 1 | 2 | 3 | 4 | 5 | ... | $n$ |
|---|---|---|---|---|---|---|---|
| Number of white squares | | | | | | | |
| Number of shaded squares | | | | | | | |

Find **a** $\sqrt{0.3025}$ (or $0.3025^{\frac{1}{2}}$)   **b** $\sqrt[3]{729\,000}$ (or $729\,000^{\frac{1}{3}}$)

. . . . . . . . . . . . . . . . . . . . . . . . . . . . . . . . . . . . . . . . . .

**a** $\sqrt{0.3025} = 0.55$, because $0.55 \times 0.55 = 0.3025$
**b** $\sqrt[3]{729\,000} = 90$, because $90 \times 90 \times 90 = 729\,000$

For questions **1** to **3**, copy and complete the table.

**1**

| $n$ | 144 | 196 | 121 | 256 | 484 | 10 000 | 2025 | 3136 | 2304 | 1296 |
|---|---|---|---|---|---|---|---|---|---|---|
| $\sqrt{n}$ | | | | | | | | | | |

**2**

| $n$ | | | | | | | | | | |
|---|---|---|---|---|---|---|---|---|---|---|
| $\sqrt{n}$ | 13 | 42 | 18 | 32 | 27 | 19 | 54 | 17 | 52 | 1000 |

**3**

| $n$ | 216 | 1000 | 512 | 8000 | 2744 | 1 000 000 | | | | | |
|---|---|---|---|---|---|---|---|---|---|---|---|
| $\sqrt[3]{n}$ | | | | | | | 7 | 13 | 18 | 11 | 25 | 30 |

**4** Solve these equations.

**a** $x^{\frac{1}{2}} = 55$          **b** $y^{\frac{1}{2}} = 70$
**c** $z^{\frac{1}{2}} = 40$          **d** $t^{\frac{1}{3}} = 40$
**e** $v^{\frac{1}{3}} = 1000$          **f** $m^3 = -27$
**g** $n^3 = -125$          **h** $q^3 = -1\,000\,000$

**5** Find the side length of
**a** a square tray of area 1521 cm²
**b** a square carpet of area 10.24 m².

Area =
1521 cm²

Area =
10.24 m²

**6** Gaynor's dog lives in a cubic kennel of volume
0.512 m³, her rabbits live in a cubic hutch of
volume 0.216 m³ and her chickens have a cubic
hen house of volume 42.875 m³. Find the side
length for each animal house.

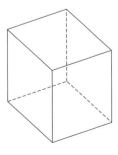

example

Simplify these, leaving your anwers in index form.
**a** $4^3 \times 4^5$      **b** $\frac{6^7}{6}$    **c** $(3^4)^4$

. . . . . . . . . . . . . . . . . . . . . . . . . . . . . . . . . . . . . . . . . . . .

**a** $4^3 \times 4^5 = 4^8$ (when multiplying the indices are added)
**b** $\frac{6^7}{6} = 6^7 \div 6^1 = 6^6$ (when dividing the indices are subtracted)
**c** $(3^4)^4 = 3^4 \times 3^4 \times 3^4 \times 3^4 = 3^{16}$

**1** Write these expressions in index form.

  **a** $3 \times 3 \times 3 \times 3$          **b** $6 \times 6 \times 6$        **c** $x \times x \times x \times x \times x \times x$
  **d** $y \times y \times y$            **e** $5 \times 5 \times 5 \times 8 \times 8$  **f** $4 \times 4 \times 6 \times 6 \times 6 \times 6$
  **g** $p \times p \times p \times q \times q \times q \times q$

**2** Evaluate these indices.

  **a** $4^3$                **b** $2^6$               **c** $10^5$
  **d** $5^4$                **e** $(-3)^4$           **f** $(-2)^7$

**3** Simplify these multiplications, leaving your answers in index form.

  **a** $2^3 \times 2^4$   **b** $5^4 \times 5^2$    **c** $3^6 \times 3^3$     **d** $x^3 \times x^5$
  **e** $y^3 \times y^9$   **f** $z^2 \times z^3 \times z^5$   **g** $p^5 \times p^4 \times p$   **h** $3r^3 \times 5r^6$

**4** Simplify these divisions, leaving your answers in index form.

  **a** $6^9 \div 6^3$   **b** $8^7 \div 8^4$     **c** $9^5 \div 9$      **d** $x^{10} \div x^4$
  **e** $z^{10} \div z^9$   **f** $12m^{10} \div 4m^2$   **g** $21n^5 \div 7n^2$   **h** $18p^5 \div 9p$

**5** Simplify these, leaving your answers in index form.

  **a** $(3^2)^4$       **b** $(5^2)^7$      **c** $(x^3)^4$
  **d** $(y^5)^3$      **e** $(2p^4)^3$

**6** Find the area of the airstrip.
  Give your answer **a** in index form
  **b** as an ordinary number.

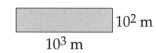

$10^2$ m
$10^3$ m

example

> Show that $5(x-2) - 3(x-4) = 2(x+1)$ is an identity.
> (That is to say true for all values of $x$.)
> ................................................................
> $5(x-2) - 3(x-4) = 5x - 10 - 3x + 12 = 2x + 2$ and
> $2(x+1) = 2x + 2$. Therefore the equality is true for all
> values of $x$.

**1** Solve these equations.

a $4n + 5 = 21$

b $5p - 7 = 18$

c $3(q + 7) = 45$

d $4(r - 2) = 36$

e $8(4x + 1) = 9(3x + 2)$

f $7(4y - 5) = 11(2y - 1)$

g $7(3z - 4) = 5(2z + 1)$

h $5(2t - 1) = 3(t + 3)$

**2** Find the value of the required variable in
these formulae.

a $V = xyz$     Find $V$ if $x = 8$, $y = 3$ and $z = 4.5$.

b $P = 2a + 2b$    Find $P$ if $a = 15$ and $b = 7$.

c $L = a + Yn$    Find $L$ if $a = 10$, $Y = 0.5$ and $n = 6$.

d $s = \frac{1}{2}at^2$      Find $s$ if $a = 10$ and $t = 1.5$.

**3** Prove that these are identities by transforming
the left-hand side.

a $4(x + 7) + 2 = 4x + 30$

b $3(z + 2) + 4z = 7z + 6$

c $5(t - 2) + 4t = 9t - 10$

d $7(u + 1) + 4(u + 6) = 11u + 31$

e $8(v + 3) + 2(v - 7) = 10v + 10$

f $5(m + 1) + 3(m - 4) = 8m - 7$

**4** Prove that these are identities by transforming
both sides.

a $4(p + 2) + 3(p + 9) = 7(p + 5)$

b $3(q + 6) + 2(q - 4) = 5(q + 2)$

c $6(r + 1) + 5(r - 10) = 11(r - 4)$

d $4(n + 3) - 2(n + 1) = 2(n + 5)$

e $7(p - 2) - 3(p + 2) = 4(p - 5)$

f $8(r - 3) - 5(r - 6) = 3(r + 2)$

example

The organisers of opinion polls select a very good sample of people to question before they predict the outcome of a general election and their predictions are often quite good. They are, however, quite wrong sometimes. Can you suggest any factor or factors that they do not allow for?

· · · · · · · · · · · · · · · · · · · · · · · · · · · · · · · · · · · · · · · · · · · · · · · · · · · · · · ·

One factor that they cannot allow for is the fact that some people always change their minds on the way to the polling station.

**1** The transport officials in London are always trying to reduce road congestion. They have offered cheaper bus and train travel and even introduced congestion charges in Central London, but further out the problem persists. Can you think of any other factors that cause the trouble further out? Look at a tube train map, does that tell you anything?

**2** Sometimes flat roofs spring a leak and often poor workmanship is conveniently blamed, but can you think of any other reasons?

**3** Speed of vehicles is well known to be one cause of road accidents, but it is still said that motorways are the safest roads. Think of a list of factors that make motorways safer. Does it mean that building more motorways might make other roads safer?

**4** A medical researcher thinks that people who suffer from frequent headaches are often people who are under stress at work. He therefore finds out the number of hours per day that they work in order to see if there is any connection. What other factors do you think he should consider?

example

Lisa often drives to her sister's house and she thinks that she uses more petrol if the journey takes longer.
She thinks that stopping and starting in traffic queues increases petrol consumption more than travelling at a faster speed does.
She recorded some details for five of her journeys.

| Journey time (h) | 2 | $2\frac{1}{4}$ | 2 | $1\frac{3}{4}$ | $2\frac{1}{2}$ |
|---|---|---|---|---|---|
| Petrol consumed (litres) | 10 | 11 | 9 | 9 | 13 |

Do you think that her hypothesis is correct?
......................................................

Yes, the figures quite clearly show that what she thinks is correct.

**1** A transport users consultative group claim that the time that passengers have to queue for tickets at their local railway station depends on the time of the day. One Thursday they recorded the waiting time at hourly intervals by observing people in the queue. They also did the same on Friday of the same week.

| Time of day | 08:00 | 09:00 | 10:00 | 11:00 | 12:00 | 13:00 | 14:00 | 15:00 | 16:00 | 17:00 | 18:00 | 19:00 | 20:00 |
|---|---|---|---|---|---|---|---|---|---|---|---|---|---|
| Queueing time in minutes (Thursday) | 4 | 2 | 1 | 0 | 0 | 0 | 1 | 0 | 1 | 3 | 3 | 1 | 0 |
| Queueing time in minutes (Friday) | 9 | 6 | 3 | 4 | 2 | 1 | 0 | 1 | 5 | 6 | 4 | 2 | 2 |

Do these figures support their hypothesis? Why is there a difference between the Thursday and Friday figures?

**example**

Obesity is always a problem and a doctor wants to collect data on two variables for his obese patients. The two variables are **i** how much exercise the patient does and **ii** the patient's diet. Do you think that he can collect data for these two variables and if so how?

He can collect data for both of these variables by asking his patients, but many people who do not exercise will not admit it. Perhaps an organised exercise program would help him to know more.

**1** For the following situations, say whether you think data could be collected on each of the variables, and if so how?

  **a** An education advisor wants to find out what affects childrens' performance at school. She decides to consider these variables.

    **i**   Natural ability     **ii** Gender     **iii** Family background
    **iv** Health     **v** How many schools the pupil has attended
    **vi** The pupil's opinion of his or her teachers
    **vii** The pupil's relationships with other pupils

  **b** The headmaster of Bank Street School wants to find out what makes his 16-plus aged pupils stay at his school or continue their studies at a college. He considers these variables.

    **i**   Gender     **ii**   Does the pupil want to be with people in his or her age group only?
    **iii** The pupils' opinion of the teachers at the school
    **iv** More freedom of hours at a college
    **v**   The distance that the pupil may have to travel
    **vi** Are better out-of-lesson amenities available at a college?

example

A physics teacher decides to investigate how many pupils between 11 and 13 would know how to fix a plug onto an electric wire. He wonders whether it depends on age and on gender. Design a suitable questionnaire sheet that he could use for the purpose.

......................................................

Here is a suitable table for his details.

| Name | Age | Gender | Answer (yes or no) |
|------|-----|--------|--------------------|
|      |     |        |                    |
|      |     |        |                    |

**1** Zoe wants to investigate how much time 11-, 12- and 13-year-olds usually spend watching television each evening. She has designed this questionnaire sheet.

| Name | Age | Gender | Is your watching time less than 1 h? | Is your watching time between 1 and 2 h? | Is your watching time more than 2 h? | Number of siblings |
|------|-----|--------|----------|----------|----------|----------|
| Tom | 11 | | | | | |
| Jake | 11 | | | | | |
| Ann | 11 | | | | | |
| Jane | 12 | | | | | |
| Kate | 12 | | | | | |
| Dave | 12 | | | | | |
| Pete | 13 | | | | | |
| Derek | 13 | | | | | |
| Jill | 13 | | | | | |

**a** How could she improve this questionnaire sheet?

**b** State three hypotheses that it could be used to test.

example

Asif recorded the temperature outside his house at midday over a two-week period.

| Day | Mon | Tue | Wed | Thu | Fri | Sat | Sun | Mon | Tue | Wed | Thu | Fri | Sat | Sun |
|---|---|---|---|---|---|---|---|---|---|---|---|---|---|---|
| Temp (°C) | 2 | 3 | 7 | 9 | 10 | 11 | 13 | 9 | 6 | 4 | 8 | 10 | 12 | 14 |

Summarise his details in a grouped frequency table. Use the inclusive intervals 1–5 °C, 6–10 °C and 11–16 °C.

· · · · · · · · · · · · · · · · · · · · · · · · · · · · · · · · · · · · · · · · · · · · · · · · · · · · · · ·

| Temperature (°C) | 1–5 | 6–10 | 11–15 |
|---|---|---|---|
| Number of days | 3 | 7 | 4 |

**1** Rajmeet recorded her driving times to work (in minutes) over a six-week period.

| Time (min) | 26 | 16 | 27 | 29 | 28 | 20 | 29 | 21 | 31 | 23 | 29 | 23 | 32 | 26 | 24 |
|---|---|---|---|---|---|---|---|---|---|---|---|---|---|---|---|
| Time (min) | 30 | 24 | 17 | 22 | 33 | 28 | 30 | 25 | 27 | 18 | 29 | 19 | 28 | 35 | 27 |

   **a** Summarise her details in a grouped frequency table.
   Use the inclusive intervals 16–20 min, 21–25 min,
   26–30 min and 31–35 min.
   **b** In which interval does the median lie?

**2** Later, Rajmeet in question **1** again recorded her driving times to work over a six-week period, but by now a bypass around a village on the way had been opened.

| Time (min) | 16 | 22 | 27 | 17 | 21 | 21 | 27 | 24 | 23 | 20 | 32 | 17 | 23 | 28 | 25 |
|---|---|---|---|---|---|---|---|---|---|---|---|---|---|---|---|
| Time (min) | 16 | 26 | 18 | 19 | 22 | 18 | 19 | 29 | 24 | 25 | 21 | 20 | 23 | 28 | 30 |

   **a** Summarise her details in the same way as you did
   in question **1**.
   **b** In which interval does the median now lie? Is this
   what you would expect?

The table shows how many meals two cafes at a seaside resort served on an August Bank Holiday weekend.

|  | Sat | Sun | Mon |
|---|---|---|---|
| **Promenade End Café** | 60 | 90 | 30 |
| **Beach View Café** | 60 | 75 | 45 |

Display the details on a comparative bar chart.

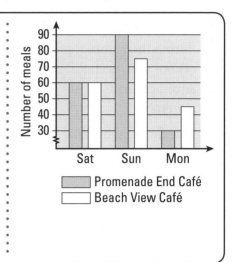

Promenade End Café
Beach View Café

**1** These are the ages of the teachers at Green Lane School.

23 24 27 28 29 32 35 36 37 38 39 41 43
44 47 48 49 51 52 54 55 57 59 61 63

Display this information on a stem-and-leaf diagram.

**2** Two icecream sellers sell their icecream on a beach over the 4 days of an Easter Holiday weekend. Their sales are shown in the table.

|  | Fri | Sat | Sun | Mon |
|---|---|---|---|---|
| Tommy's Ices | 100 | 75 | 75 | 50 |
| Jim's Icecreams | 50 | 100 | 100 | 50 |

Copy and complete the comparative bar chart and the two pie charts.

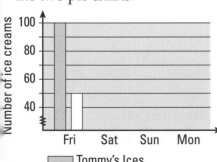

Tommy's Ices
Jim's Icecreams

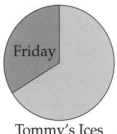

Tommy's Ices

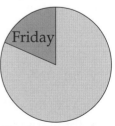

Jim's Icecreams

example

The Year 11 pupils at West Park School were asked three times during the summer term what they wanted to do in the new school year. Some changed their minds as the term went on and their answers are shown. Show the details on a time trend bar chart.

Was there an overall trend?

|  | April | May | June |
|---|---|---|---|
| Stay at school (%) | 30 | 30 | 40 |
| Go to a college (%) | 30 | 40 | 40 |
| Go out to work (%) | 40 | 30 | 20 |

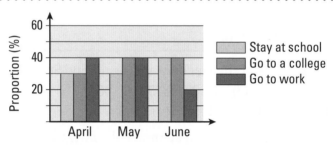

Yes, more decided that they wanted to continue in education as the term went on.

**1** This table shows modes of transport for students at High Lane School after they were shown a film about how to keep fit.

|  | March | | | April | | | May | | |
|---|---|---|---|---|---|---|---|---|---|
|  | **Walk** | **Cycle** | **Car** | **Walk** | **Cycle** | **Car** | **Walk** | **Cycle** | **Car** |
| Boys (%) | 40 | 20 | 40 | 40 | 30 | 30 | 40 | 40 | 20 |
| Girls (%) | 20 | 20 | 60 | 30 | 20 | 50 | 40 | 20 | 40 |

Display the data on
**a** three comparison bar charts, one for each month
**b** two trend bar charts, one for boys and one for girls.

> **example**
>
> Find the ratio of 300 m to 0.54 km in its simplest form.
> ..............................................................
> 300 m : 0.54 km = 300 m : 540 m = 300 : 540 = 30 : 54 = 5 : 9

For questions **1** to **3**, express each ratio in its simplest form.

**1 a** 10:12    **b** 8:14    **c** 12:15    **d** 15:21    **e** 16:20
   **f** 20:28    **g** 20:25    **h** 12:18    **i** 24:32    **j** 27:45

**2 a** 10:8    **b** 9:6    **c** 28:16    **d** 45:40    **e** 54:48
   **f** 45:36    **g** 56:49    **h** 105:60    **i** 125:75    **j** 135:90

**3 a** 8:10:12    **b** 12:15:21    **c** 8:12:20    **d** 15:25:40
   **e** 18:24:54    **f** 14:35:49    **g** 30:45:75    **h** 24:36:96

**4** Express each of these ratios in the form $1:n$.
   **a** 6:18    **b** 12:60    **c** 15:75    **d** 18:54    **e** 25:125
   **f** 36:144    **g** 75:225    **h** 16:96    **i** 18:108    **j** 16:112

**5** Express each of these ratios in their simplest form.
   **a** 1.5:2          **b** 1.2:3          **c** 4.5:12
   **d** 7.5:24        **e** 32 cm:0.4 m      **f** 125 g:0.2 kg
   **g** 900 ml:1.5 litres    **h** 540 m:3 km

**6** The table shows the performance of four members of
   an archery club. Copy and complete the table.

| Member | Number of bull's eyes | Number of shots | Ratio of bull's eyes to shots | Ratio as a decimal | Order of merit |
|---|---|---|---|---|---|
| Jamil | 6 | 8 | | | |
| Lisa | 7 | 10 | | | |
| Layla | 9 | 15 | | | |
| Mike | 13 | 20 | | | |

Divide £20 in the ratio 2:3:5.

· · · · · · · · · · · · · · · · · · · · · · · · · · · · · · · · · · · · · · · · · · · · ·

$2 + 3 + 5 = 10$ therefore one 'share' $= £20 \div 10$ or £2.
So 2 shares is $2 \times 2$ or £4, 3 shares is $3 \times 2$ or £6 and 5 shares is $5 \times 2$ or £10.

**1** Divide each of these quantities in the ratio given.
  **a** £90 in the ratio 2:3          **b** £108 in the ratio 5:7
  **c** 450 g in the ratio 7:8       **d** 500 g in the ratio 3:5:12
  **e** 210 cm in the ratio 2:5:7    **f** £1000 in the ratio 12:13:15

**2** Divide each of these quantities in the ratio given.
  **a** £18 in the ratio 7:8         **b** 24 kg in the ratio 7:9
  **c** £7 in the ratio 3:5:6        **d** 9 m in the ratio 4:5:6
  **e** 15 kg in the ratio 5:7:8     **f** £36 in the ratio 5:7:13

**3 a** The three sides of an isosceles triangle have lengths
    in the ratio 10:10:13. If the perimeter of the triangle
    is 132 cm, find the three side lengths.
  **b** Find the three angles of a triangle if they are in the
    ratio 9:9:22.

**4** There are two railway routes from London to Taunton
  and the distances are in the ratio of 7:8. If the distance
  is 224 km via the shorter route, how far is it by the
  longer route?

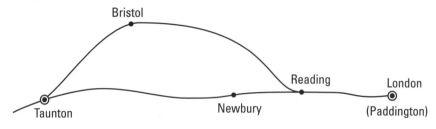

> If 300 litres of heating oil cost £360, find **a** the cost of 500 litres **b** the number of litres that can be bought for £150.
>
> . . . . . . . . . . . . . . . . . . . . . . . . . . . . . . . . . . . . . . . . . . . . . . . . . .
>
> **a** The cost is $\frac{500}{300} \times 360 = £600$.
> **b** The quantity is $\frac{150}{360} \times 300 = 125$ litres.

**1** Afiya drives for 90 km in her car and finds that she has used up 6 litres of petrol.

  **a** How far can she expect to drive on **i** 8 litres **ii** 15 litres **iii** 12 litres **iv** 5 litres **v** 4.5 litres of petrol?

  **b** How many litres should she expect to consume if she drives **i** 105 km **ii** 135 km **iii** 240 km **iv** 60 km **v** 37.5 km?

**2** Dave is a long distance runner and he trains by running several kilometres at a steady pace. It takes him 45 min to run 10 km.

  **a** Find how long it takes him to run
    **i** 4 km **ii** 6 km **iii** 14 km **iv** 22 km **v** 26 km

  **b** Find how far he will run in
    **i** 36 min **ii** 54 min **iii** 1 h 30 min **iv** 1 h 12 min **v** 1 h 21 min

**3** Copy and complete the conversion table.

| Miles | 10 | 25 | 45 | 105 | 37.5 | 62.5 | | | | | |
|---|---|---|---|---|---|---|---|---|---|---|---|
| Kilometers | 16 | | | | | | 24 | 56 | 120 | 200 | 140 |

**4** If 300 litres of heating oil cost £360, find

  **a** the cost of **i** 400 litres **ii** 250 litres **iii** 180 litres **iv** 120 litres **v** 80 litres

  **b** how many litres could be bought for **i** £420 **ii** £270 **iii** £108 **iv** £210 **v** £126

**example**

A bus has 20 passengers sitting downstairs and 16 sitting upstairs. Find **a** the ratio of those sitting downstairs to those sitting upstairs **b** the proportion sitting downstairs **c** the proportion sitting upstairs.

· · · · · · · · · · · · · · · · · · · · · · · · · · · · · · · · · · · · · · · · · · · · · · · · · ·

**a** The ratio is $20:16$ or $5:4$.

**b** The proportion sitting downstairs $= \frac{20}{36}$ or $\frac{5}{9}$.

**c** The proportion sitting upstairs is $\frac{16}{36}$ or $\frac{4}{9}$.

**1** Copy and complete these details about the students in Year 7 at Willow Bank School.

| Class | Number of boys | Number of girls | Total | Ratio | Proportion of boys | Proportion of girls |
|-------|----------------|-----------------|-------|-------|--------------------|--------------------|
| 7A | 9 | 16 | | | | |
| 7B | 9 | 11 | | | | |
| 7C | 13 | 12 | | | | |

**2** Joanne travels to see her aunt. She travels $\frac{2}{7}$ of the way on a bus and then, after a very quick connection, the rest of the way by train.

**a** Find

   **i** the fraction of the distance that she travels by train

   **ii** the ratio of the distance travelled by bus to that travelled by train

   **iii** the distance travelled by train if the distance on the bus is 30 km

   **iv** the total distance that she travels.

**b** If she spends $\frac{3}{8}$ of her journey time on the bus, find

   **i** the fraction of her journey time that she spends on the train

   **ii** the ratio of the time spent on the bus to that spent on the train

   **iii** the time that she spends on the bus if she spends 1 h and 5 min on the train

   **iv** the total time that her journey takes.

**a** Jim's weekly wage is £225, but he is to get a 4% pay rise. What will his new pay be?

**b** Jill buys a piano for £1800, but that is the price at a sale after a reduction of 25%. What was the original price?

. . . . . . . . . . . . . . . . . . . . . . . . . . . . . . . . . . . . . . . . . . . .

**a** His new wage is $\frac{104}{100} \times £225 = £234$.

**b** The original price was $1800 \times \frac{100}{75} = £2400$.

**1** Calculate these percentage changes.

   **a** Increase £80 by 25%    **b** Increase £75 by 12%

   **c** Increase 360 m by 15%    **d** Decrease 450 g by 12%

   **e** Decrease 120 kg by 4%    **f** Decrease 90 cm by 8%

**2** Copy and complete the table about Jane's wages.

| Wage in 2006 | Wage in 2007 (5% more than in 2006) | Wage in 2008 (4% more than in 2007) | Wage in 2009 (10% more than in 2008) |
|---|---|---|---|
| £200 | | | |

**3** Copy and complete the table about Bob's dramatic weight loss programme.

| Weight on 1 Jan | Weight on 1 Feb (20% less than on 1 Jan) | Weight on 1 Mar (10% less than on 1 Feb) | Weight on 1 Apr (15% less than on 1 Mar) |
|---|---|---|---|
| 125 kg | | | |

**4** For each of these find the original price. The price given is a sale price after the reduction quoted.

   **a** A bike, £180 after a 25% reduction.

   **b** A television, £510 after a 15% reduction.

   **c** A table lamp, £30.60 after a 15% reduction.

   **d** A DVD player, £57.20 after a 12% reduction.

> example
>
> The catalogue price for a certain cooker is £150, but in a sale it is priced at £108. Find the percentage reduction.
> ............................................................................
> The actual reduction is £150 − £108 = £42, therefore the percentage reduction in $\frac{42}{150} \times 100\% = 28\%$

**1** Express each of your answers as **i** a fraction in its simplest form **ii** a decimal **iii** a percentage.

  **a** A farmer has 40 sheep and 14 are black. What proportion are black?

  **b** In a game a dice was thrown 45 times and six was the score 9 times. What proportion of the scores were sixes?

  **c** Out of 30 pupils in Class 8A, 9 cycle to school. What proportion cycle to school?

  **d** There are 56 passengers on a bus and 42 of them are sitting downstairs. What proportion are sitting downstairs?

**2** Copy and complete the table of details about a sale.

| Article | Normal price | Sales price | Reduction | Reduction as a percentage of the normal price |
|---|---|---|---|---|
| Keyboard | £150 | £126 | | |
| Chest of drawers | £112 | £84 | | |
| Table | £125 | £100 | | |
| Microwave oven | £75 | £63 | | |
| Washing machine | £300 | £246 | | |
| Computer | £270 | £229.50 | | |
| Chair | £28 | £18.20 | | |
| Video camera | £96 | £84 | | |

**example**

Find a simplified expression for the perimeter of the rectangle.

$3a+2b$

$4a-b$

. . . . . . . . . . . . . . . . . . . . . . . . . . . . . .

The perimeter is
$$3a + 2b + 4a - b + 3a + 2b + 4a - b = 14a + 2b$$

**1** Find a simplified expression for the perimeter of each of these triangles.

**a**

$x+3y$ $3x+2y$

$2x+y$

**b**

$4u-v$

**c**

$6m+n$

**2** Find a simplified expression for each missing length on these isosceles triangles.

**a**

**b**

**3** Write an algebraic expression using brackets for the shaded areas in each of these shapes.

**a**

$4x+2$

$2x$

**b**

←— $4y$ —→

$6$

$8$

**c**

$2$ $3z$

$12$

**4** Expand the brackets in each answer to question **3**.

**5 a** Write an algebraic expression using brackets for the area of this shape.

**b** Remove the brackets and simplify.

$a-1$

$3$

$3$

$2a+3$

Simplify **a** $\dfrac{x}{6}+\dfrac{5x}{9}$ **b** $\dfrac{5}{t}-\dfrac{3}{t^2}$

. . . . . . . . . . . . . . . . . . . . . . . . . . . . . . . . . . . . . . . . . . . . . . .

**a** $\dfrac{x}{6}+\dfrac{5x}{9}=\dfrac{3x}{18}+\dfrac{10x}{18}=\dfrac{13x}{18}$

**b** $\dfrac{5}{t}-\dfrac{3}{t^2}=\dfrac{5t}{t^2}-\dfrac{3}{t^2}=\dfrac{(5t-3)}{t^2}$

**1** Work these out, simplifying your answer where required.

**a** $\dfrac{1}{7}+\dfrac{5}{7}$    **b** $\dfrac{3}{5}+\dfrac{1}{5}$    **c** $\dfrac{3}{10}+\dfrac{1}{10}$    **d** $\dfrac{9}{10}-\dfrac{1}{10}$

**e** $\dfrac{7}{12}-\dfrac{5}{12}$    **f** $\dfrac{13}{15}-\dfrac{4}{15}$    **g** $\dfrac{11}{15}+\dfrac{1}{15}$    **h** $\dfrac{5}{8}+\dfrac{1}{8}$

**i** $\dfrac{7}{12}+\dfrac{1}{12}$    **j** $\dfrac{3}{20}+\dfrac{13}{20}$    **k** $\dfrac{19}{25}-\dfrac{4}{25}$    **l** $\dfrac{19}{30}-\dfrac{7}{30}$

**2** Simplify these.

**a** $\dfrac{x}{3}+\dfrac{y}{3}$    **b** $\dfrac{u}{5}+\dfrac{v}{5}$    **c** $\dfrac{m}{6}-\dfrac{n}{6}$    **d** $\dfrac{p}{7}-\dfrac{q}{7}$

**e** $\dfrac{x}{4}+\dfrac{2x}{4}$    **f** $\dfrac{3y}{5}+\dfrac{2y}{5}$    **g** $\dfrac{4z}{7}+\dfrac{3z}{7}$    **h** $\dfrac{5}{x}+\dfrac{3}{x}$

**i** $\dfrac{8}{y}+\dfrac{2}{y}$    **j** $\dfrac{7}{z}-\dfrac{3}{z}$    **k** $\dfrac{15}{t}-\dfrac{8}{t}$    **l** $\dfrac{25}{u}-\dfrac{13}{u}$

**3** Calculate these.

**a** $\dfrac{2}{5}+\dfrac{3}{10}$    **b** $\dfrac{2}{3}+\dfrac{4}{15}$    **c** $\dfrac{1}{3}+\dfrac{4}{9}$    **d** $\dfrac{2}{5}+\dfrac{3}{8}$

**e** $\dfrac{4}{5}-\dfrac{5}{8}$    **f** $\dfrac{5}{6}-\dfrac{1}{4}$    **g** $\dfrac{7}{8}-\dfrac{3}{10}$    **h** $\dfrac{5}{9}-\dfrac{1}{6}$

**i** $\dfrac{9}{10}-\dfrac{4}{15}$    **j** $\dfrac{3}{10}+\dfrac{2}{15}$    **k** $\dfrac{7}{20}+\dfrac{1}{30}$    **l** $\dfrac{5}{8}-\dfrac{1}{12}$

**4** Simplify these fractions.

**a** $\dfrac{x}{3}+\dfrac{5x}{6}$    **b** $\dfrac{y}{3}+\dfrac{2y}{9}$    **c** $\dfrac{z}{2}+\dfrac{5z}{8}$    **d** $\dfrac{4m}{5}-\dfrac{m}{10}$

**e** $\dfrac{5n}{4}-\dfrac{n}{8}$    **f** $\dfrac{3p}{2}-\dfrac{p}{3}$    **g** $\dfrac{2q}{5}-\dfrac{q}{6}$    **h** $\dfrac{x}{3}+\dfrac{3x}{4}$

**i** $\dfrac{y}{3}+\dfrac{4y}{5}$    **j** $\dfrac{z}{6}+\dfrac{4z}{9}$    **k** $\dfrac{7t}{10}-\dfrac{2t}{15}$    **l** $\dfrac{2u}{5}-\dfrac{u}{6}$

example

Make $a$ the subject of the formula $L = 4(a + b + c)$.

$L = 4(a + b + c)$, therefore $(a + b + c) = \dfrac{L}{4}$, so $a = \dfrac{L}{4} - b - c$.

**1** By substituting the given values to form an equation, find the required variable in each of these formulae.

**a** $s = \dfrac{d}{t}$    Find   **i** $d$ if $s = 20$ and $t = 7$
                        **ii** $t$ if $d = 150$ and $s = 5$.

**b** $e = \dfrac{360}{n}$    Find $n$ if     **i** $e = 5$
                            **ii** $e = 8$
                            **iii** $e = 20$.

**c** $v = u + at$ Find   **i** $u$ if $v = 10$, $a = 1.5$ and $t = 4$
   **ii** $a$ if $v = 12$, $u = 3$ and $t = 6$ **iii** $t$ if $v = 20$, $u = 4$ and $a = 0.5$.

**d** $S = 180(n - 2)$
   Find $n$ if **i** $S = 360$     **ii** $S = 1260$     **iii** $S = 2340$.

**2** The perimeter ($p$) of the isosceles triangle is given by the formula $p = 2x + y$.
**a** Find $x$ if $p = 50$ and $y = 24$.
**b** Find $y$ if $p = 65$ and $x = 25$.

**3** The surface area ($S$) of a cube is given by the formula $S = 6a^2$. Find $a$ if $S$ is
   **a** 54        **b** 150        **c** 0.24          **d** 0.96

**4** Make $x$ the subject of each of these formulae.
   **a** $p = q(x + y)$      **b** $m = n(w + x)$      **c** $t = u(x - y)$
   **d** $m = n(x - 3)$      **e** $m = \frac{1}{3}(x + y)$      **f** $p = \frac{1}{4}(x - y)$
   **g** $u = 2(x - y)$      **h** $v = 5(x + y)$      **i** $m = np(x + y)$
   **j** $p = qr(x - y)$      **k** $u = 3v(x - y)$      **l** $m = 5n(x + y)$

## 13d Solving linear equations

Solve the equation $\dfrac{(5x-4)}{11} = \dfrac{(3x+1)}{10}$

........................................................

$\dfrac{(5x-4)}{11} = \dfrac{(3x+1)}{10}$ therefore $10(5x-4) = 11(3x+1)$, therefore

$50x - 40 = 33x + 11$, therefore $17x = 51$, so $x = 3$.

For questions **1** and **2**, solve the equations.

**1 a** $\dfrac{x}{5} = 13$      **b** $\dfrac{y}{15} = 6$      **c** $\dfrac{v}{5} + 4 = 10$

  **d** $\dfrac{w}{7} + 11 = 16$    **e** $\dfrac{m}{5} - 9 = 7$    **f** $\dfrac{2n}{3} - 5 = 17$

  **g** $\dfrac{(2r-1)}{3} = 15$    **h** $\dfrac{(3s+2)}{4} = 5$

**2 a** $\dfrac{15}{x} = 3$      **b** $\dfrac{60}{y} = 15$      **c** $\dfrac{25}{u} + 4 = 9$      **d** $\dfrac{35}{v} + 2 = 9$

  **e** $\dfrac{45}{w} - 6 = 9$    **f** $\dfrac{54}{m} - 2 = 7$    **g** $\dfrac{28}{(q-3)} = 7$    **h** $\dfrac{90}{(r-1)} = 15$

**3** Solve these equations by cross multiplying.

  **a** $\dfrac{(5x-4)}{6} = \dfrac{(2x+1)}{5}$    **b** $\dfrac{(2y-3)}{7} = \dfrac{(y+3)}{8}$    **c** $\dfrac{(5t-2)}{8} = \dfrac{(4t+1)}{9}$

  **d** $\dfrac{(2u+1)}{9} = \dfrac{(u+6)}{10}$    **e** $\dfrac{(3v-5)}{4} = \dfrac{(2v-3)}{3}$    **f** $\dfrac{(2n-1)}{7} = \dfrac{n}{4}$

**4** Jisanne and Ayo are keen cyclists. Jisanne cycles $x - 45$ km
from Manchester to Preston in 3 h, Ayo cycles $x + 15$ km from
Manchester to Wolverhampton in 7 h. They both cycle at the same
speed. Jisanne's speed can be written
as $\dfrac{x-45}{3}$.

  **a** Form an equation in $x$.

  **b** Solve your equation for $x$.

  **c** Find the distance from

    **i** Manchester to Preston

    **ii** Manchester to Wolverhampton.

  **d** Find the speed that they both cycle at.

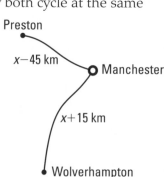

**example**

Solve the equation $z^2 - 2z = 120$ by a trial-and-improvement method.

.................................................

Try $z = 10$: $10^2 - 2 \times 10 = 100 - 20 = 80$ (too small)
Try $z = 15$: $15^2 - 2 \times 15 = 225 - 30 = 195$ (too large)
Try $z = 12$: $12^2 - 2 \times 12 = 144 - 24 = 120$ (correct)

For questions **1** to **3**, find a positive solution to the equation using a trial-and-improvement method.

**1 a** $x^2 + x = 132$    **b** $y^2 + y = 210$    **c** $z^2 + z = 380$
   **d** $u^2 - u = 156$    **e** $v^2 - v = 182$    **f** $x^2 + 2x = 120$
   **g** $t^2 - 3t = 270$    **h** $s^2 - 4v = 320$

**2 a** $x^3 + x = 520$    **b** $y^3 + y = 222$    **c** $z^3 - z = 1716$
   **d** $m^3 - m = 1320$    **e** $n^3 - n = 3360$    **f** $x^3 + 2x = 357$
   **g** $q^3 - 3q = 110$    **h** $r^3 - 10r = 7800$

**3 a** $2^x = 256$    **b** $3^y = 2187$    **c** $5^z = 3125$
   **d** $4^t = 4096$    **e** $6^u = 1296$    **f** $7^v = 16807$

**4** The buses owned by a certain company each have
$n + 2$ seats, and $n$ such buses have 3720 seats altogether.
   **a** Form an equation in $n$.
   **b** Solve your equation for $n$.
   **c** Find the number of seats in each bus.

**5** It is $x^2 + 1$ km from Joanne's house to Julie's house and one week Joanne makes $x$ journeys between the two to visit Julie when she is ill. If she travels 30 km altogether, find
   **a** the value of $x$ from an equation
   **b** the distance between their houses.

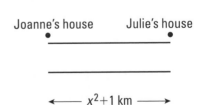

# 13f Graphs of implicit functions

**example**

Make $y$ the subject of the equation $x + 2y = 6$ and draw its graph.

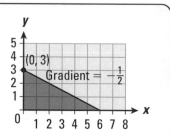

$x + 2y = 6$ therefore

$2y = 6 - x$, so $y = 3 - \frac{1}{2}x$

**1** Rearrange these equations to make $y$ the subject.

**a** $y + x = 10$   **b** $y - 5 = 3x$   **c** $y - 4 = \frac{1}{2}x$

**d** $y + 3 = 5x$   **e** $y + 4 = \frac{1}{2}x$   **f** $y - 3x - 2 = 0$

**g** $y + 2x - 4 = 0$   **h** $2y - x = 5$   **i** $2y - 3x = 1$

**j** $3y + 2x = 3$   **k** $4y + 3x = 7$   **l** $6y + x = 3$

**2** For each part, plot the three given graph lines on a copy of the grid illustrated and give the coordinates of any points where the lines intersect.

**a** $x + y = 5$, $2y - x = 4$, $2x - y = 1$

**b** $x + y = 7$, $2y - x = 8$, $2x - y = 2$

**c** $x + y = 8$, $2y - x = 1$, $2x - y = 1$

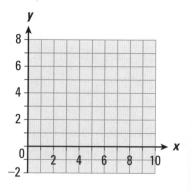

**3 a** Rearrange the equation $2y - x = 6$ so as to make $y$ the subject.

**b** Copy and complete the table and draw the graph for the equation. (Use a grid the same as that shown for question **2**.)

| $x =$ | 0 | 4 | 8 |
|-------|---|---|---|
| $y =$ |   |   |   |

**c** Find from your graph

**i** the value of $y$ when $x = 2$

**ii** the value of $x$ when $y = 6$.

# 13g Algebra and proportion

Some masses are placed on the end of a spring and the table shows the extensions produced. Are the masses all the same?

| Number of masses | 0 | 2 | 3 | 7 |
|---|---|---|---|---|
| Extension (cm) | 0 | 3 | 4.5 | 10.5 |

Yes, because $\dfrac{3}{2} = \dfrac{4.5}{3} = \dfrac{10.5}{7} = 1.5$ cm per mass.

For questions **1** to **3**, find whether or not the figures are in direct proportion. If they are, plot the figures on a graph and give the equation of the line.

**1** Mr. Bhatti drives along a motorway and he times himself after certain distances.

| Time | 0 | 32 min | 48 min | 1 h 20 min | 1 h 36 min | 2 h |
|---|---|---|---|---|---|---|
| Distance (km) | 0 | 40 | 60 | 100 | 120 | 150 |

**2** A battery is being charged and the table shows the voltage after various times.

| Time | 0 | 42 min | 1 h 36 min | 2 h | 2 h 30 min | 3 h |
|---|---|---|---|---|---|---|
| Voltage | 0 V | 0.35 V | 0.8 V | 1 V | 1.25 V | 1.5 V |

**3** The table shows the number of sides and diagonals for certain polygons.

| Number of sides | 8 | 9 | 10 | 12 |
|---|---|---|---|---|
| Number of diagonals | 20 | 27 | 35 | 54 |

**4** This pair of triangles is similar, that is to say one is an enlargement of the other. Find the missing sides.

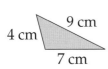
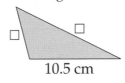

Mrs. Singh made a return journey in her car to the supermarket.

Owing to heavy traffic it took her 45 min to get there. She spent 45 min at the supermarket and then drove home in 15 min.

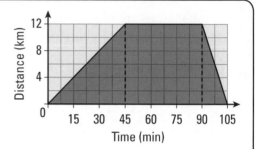

Find **a** her average speed on the way to the supermarket.
    **b** her average speed on the way home.

. . . . . . . . . . . . . . . . . . . . . . . . . . . . . . . . . . . . . . . . . . . . . . . . . .

**a** Average speed = distance (km) ÷ time (h) = $12 \div \frac{3}{4}$
    = $12 \times \frac{4}{3} = 16$ km/h.

**b** Average speed = distance (km) ÷ time (h) = $12 \div \frac{1}{4}$
    = $12 \times 4 = 48$ km/h.

**1** Marie goes to a craft fair. She walks there and stops at her friend's house on the way. After visiting the fair she is given a lift home.

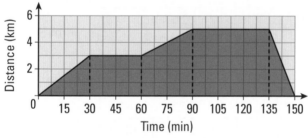

**a** How long does she spend at
  **i** her friend's house    **ii** the craft fair?

**b** What is her average speed between
  **i** leaving home and reaching her friend's house
  **ii** her friend's house and the craft fair
  **iii** leaving the craft fair and returning home?

Copy and complete the triangle. Measure the lengths of any missing sides and the size of any missing angles.

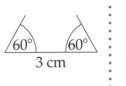

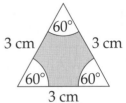

For questions **1** and **2**, copy the drawings to full scale and complete the triangles. Measure the lengths of any missing sides and the size of any missing angles.

**1 a**

7 cm

**b**

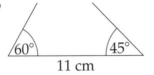

11 cm

**c**

3 cm

**2 a**

2.5 cm

6.5 cm

**b**

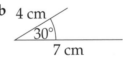

4 cm

7 cm

**c**

10 cm

7 cm

**3** For each of these triangles find the unknown angle and then construct the triangle to full scale. Measure the lengths of any missing sides.

**a**

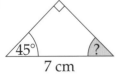

45°

7 cm

**b**

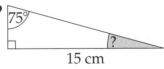

75°

15 cm

**c**

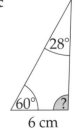

28°

60°

6 cm

Construct a triangle ABC such that AB = 2.5 cm, AC = 2 cm and BC = 1.5 cm.

. . . . . . . . . . . . . . . . . . . . . . . . . . . . . . . . . . . . . . . . . . . . . . . .

Draw AB equal to 2.5 cm. Set the compass points 2 cm apart and draw an arc with the metal point at A.
Set the compass points 1.5 cm apart and draw an arc with the metal point at B. C is where the arcs cross so AC and BC can be drawn.

**a** A ‾‾‾2.5 cm‾‾‾ B  **b** ✕   **c**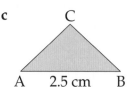

A ‾‾‾2.5 cm‾‾‾ B

**1** Construct these triangles. Measure the angles and check that they total 180°.
  **a** AB = 8 cm, AC = 6 cm, BC = 10 cm.
  **b** AB = 7 cm, AC = BC = 4 cm.
  **c** AB = 5.5 cm, AC = 4 cm, BC = 5 cm.

**2** A wire stay of length 6.5 m is supporting a pole and the end of the stay is 4 m from the foot of the pole.
  **a** Using a scale of 1 cm to represent 50 cm, construct a scale drawing of the stay and the pole.
  **b** Find from your drawing
    **i** the height of the pole
    **ii** the angle that the stay makes with the ground.

**example**

Bisect an angle of 60°

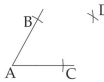
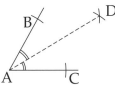

With the metal point of the compass at A, draw an arc through B and C. Now place the metal point at each of B and C and draw a pair of arcs that cross at D. Finally join DA.

**1** Draw and label these lines (AB). Using a compass, construct the perpendicular bisector of each line.
**a** AB = 10 cm      **b** AB = 6 cm      **c** AB = 8.4 cm
**d** AB = 96 mm      **e** AB = 120 mm      **f** AB = 0.2 m

**2** Using a compass, construct the bisector for each of these angles.
**a** 70°      **b** 50°      **c** 64°
**d** 120°      **e** 144°      **f** 108°

**3** Construct the equilateral triangle illustrated. Construct a perpendicular line from C down to AB and measure the height of C above AB.

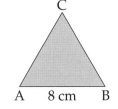

**4** Construct, to full scale, each of these shapes by using two of the triangles illustrated.
**a** A square
**b** An enlargement of the triangle
**c** A parallelogram
Mark on your drawings any line(s) of symmetry.

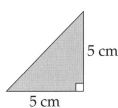

Draw the locus of the points that are 3 cm from a point A.

· · · · · · · · · · · · · · · · · · · · · · · · · · · · · · · · · · · · · · · · · · ·

The points lie on a circle of radius 3 cm with its centre at A.

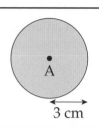

3 cm

**1** Draw the line AB to scale. Draw the locus of the points that are **a** 4 cm from A **b** 3 cm from B. Join the points where the loci intersect to A and B.
**c** Name the type of quadrilateral you have formed.

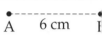

A    6 cm    B

**2** The diagram shows a new football pitch that is 80 m long. Draw the diagram using a scale of 1 cm to represent 5 m. Draw the locus for where the halfway line will have to be marked.

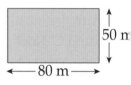

50 m

←— 80 m —→

**3** A station for a new tramway is being built. One platform is built and the other must be of equal length, parallel to it and 4.5 m away. Using a scale of 0.5 cm to represent 2 m, draw a locus for the position of the other platform.

4.5 m

3 m

←————— 24 m —————→

**4** A triangle ABC has an area of 15 cm² and the base, AB, of the triangle is 6 cm long. Draw the line AB and the locus of the point C.

**5** Draw each of these angles POQ.
**a** 90°   **b** 56°   **c** 78°   **d** 150°   **e** 130°   **f** 112°
For each case draw the locus of the points that are equidistant from OP and OQ.

example

Find the bearing of **a** B from A   **b** C from A.

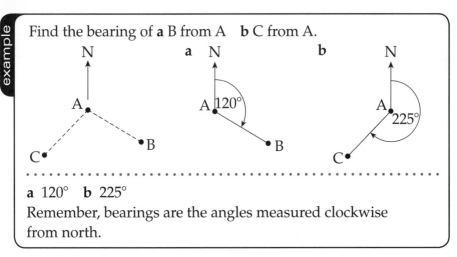

**a** 120°   **b** 225°

Remember, bearings are the angles measured clockwise from north.

**1** Find the bearing of each place from the town centre.

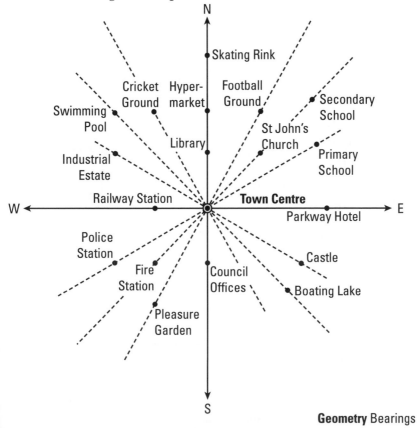

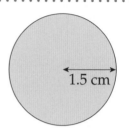

**example**

A circle has a radius of 1.5 cm. Find **a** its circumference **b** its area.

**a** Circumference = $\pi \times$ diameter
$= \pi \times 2 \times$ radius
$= 3.14 \times 2 \times 1.5$
$= 9.42$ cm

**b** Area = $\pi \times$ radius squared
$= 3.14 \times 1.5 \times 1.5 = 7.065$ cm²

1.5 cm

**1** Copy and complete the table.

| | Diameter | Radius | Circumference | Area | | Diameter | Radius | Circumference | Area |
|---|---|---|---|---|---|---|---|---|---|
| **a** | 6 cm | | | | **f** | 0.1 m | | | |
| **b** | 20 cm | | | | **g** | | | 15.7 cm | |
| **c** | 0.04 m | | | | **h** | | | 94.2 mm | |
| **d** | | 8 cm | | | **i** | | | 314 mm | |
| **e** | | 0.3 m | | | **j** | 4 km | | | |

**2** The diagram shows a clock with second, minute and hour hands. Find

**a** the circumference that the top of each hand travels in one hour

**b** the speed in cm/s that the end of each hand moves at.

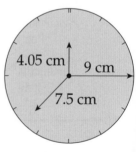

4.05 cm  9 cm

7.5 cm

**3** Find the shaded areas in each of these shapes.

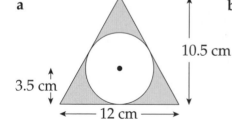

**a**

10.5 cm

3.5 cm

12 cm

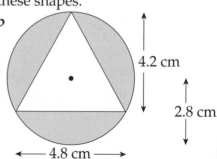

**b**

4.2 cm

2.8 cm

4.8 cm

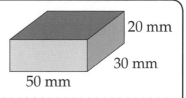

**example**

Find the surface area of this cuboid.

20 mm

30 mm

50 mm

The surface area $= (2 \times 50 \times 30) + (2 \times 50 \times 20) + (2 \times 30 \times 20)$
$= 3000 + 2000 + 1200 = 6200 \, \text{mm}^2$

**1** Find the surface area of each of these cuboids.
   **a** length $= 5\,\text{cm}$   width $= 4\,\text{cm}$   height $= 2\,\text{cm}$
   **b** length $= 8\,\text{cm}$   width $= 4.5\,\text{cm}$   height $= 2.5\,\text{cm}$
   **c** length $= 40\,\text{mm}$  width $= 30\,\text{mm}$  height $= 15\,\text{mm}$
   **d** length $= 0.4\,\text{m}$  width $= 0.25\,\text{m}$  height $= 0.2\,\text{m}$
   **e** length $= 0.5\,\text{m}$  width $= 0.5\,\text{m}$  height $= 0.4\,\text{m}$

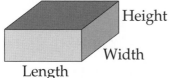

Height

Width

Length

**2** Calculate the side length of the cube if
   its surface area is
   **a** $726\,\text{cm}^2$   **b** $1536\,\text{cm}^2$
   **c** $73.5\,\text{cm}^2$  **d** $8.64\,\text{m}^2$

**3 a** Calculate the surface area of each prism.
   **b** Draw a net of each prism.

**i**

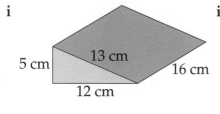

5 cm   13 cm   16 cm
12 cm

**ii**

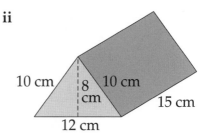

10 cm   8 cm   10 cm
12 cm   15 cm

Look at the cuboid in the worked example for Homework **14g**
and find its volume.

. . . . . . . . . . . . . . . . . . . . . . . . . . . . . . . . . . . . . . . . . . . . . . . .

The volume $= 50 \times 30 \times 20 = 30\,000$ mm³

**1** Find the volume of each cuboid in question **1** of Homework **14g**.

**2** For each of these prisms find
   **i** the area of the triangular end
   **ii** the volume of the prism.
   **iii** Draw the net for each prism. (Use any convenient scale.)

**a**

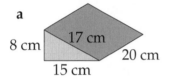

**b**

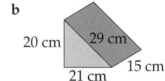

**c**

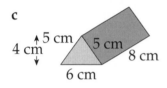

**d**

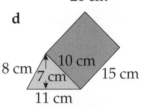

**3** For each of these find    **a** 10 cm ↕
   **i** the area of the circular end             **b** 25 mm ↕
   **ii** the volume of the cylinder.    40 cm         50 mm

**4** The net of a prism is shown.
   Find the volume of the prism.

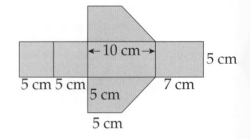

example

Joanne recorded the number of minutes by which her school bus was late over a 2 week period.

2 1 0 3 1 3 6 2 0 1 5

Find **a** the mode **b** the median **c** the range for these times.

. . . . . . . . . . . . . . . . . . . . . . . . . . . . . . . . . . . . . . . . . . . . . . . . . . . . .

Arranged in order the figures are

0 0 1 1 1 2 2 3 3 5

**a** The mode is 1, because it occurs more frequently than any other number.

**b** The median is $\dfrac{(1+2)}{2} = 1.5$. (1 and 2 are the 'middle' terms.)

**c** The range is $5 - 0 = 5$. (Largest term minus smallest term)

**1** Over a 2-week period the numbers of absent pupils in Candace's class were

1 2 0 3 2 3 1 2 0 4

Find **a** the mode **b** the median **c** the range.

**2** There are 30 tutor groups at High Park School and these are the numbers of students in each group.

24  19  22  26  29  31  30  25  33  16  32  17  15  20  28  24
26  22  25  17  21  24  27  15  23  28  30  18  31  29

**a** Copy and complete this grouped frequency table.

| Class interval (number of students) | 15–19 (incl.) | 20–24 (incl.) | 25–29 (incl.) | 30–35 (incl.) |
|---|---|---|---|---|
| Number of tutor groups | | | | |

Use your table to find

**b** the modal class

**c** the class interval in which the median lies.

## 15b More averages

George played for his football team in all five matches of a cup contest. The numbers of goals he scored in each match were 1 0 3 1 and 2. Find the mean number of goals that he scored.

. . . . . . . . . . . . . . . . . . . . . . . . . . . . . . . . . . . . . . . . . . . . . . .

The total number of goals is $1 + 0 + 3 + 1 + 2 = 7$, therefore the mean number of goals is $7 \div 5$ or 1.4.

For questions **1** to **3**, find the mean.

**1** A train consists of six coaches and the numbers of passengers in each coach are 43, 55, 61, 63, 53 and 37.

**2** There are eight classes at Holly Park Junior School and the numbers of children in each class are 25, 27, 28, 31, 26, 29, 26 and 24.

**3** The times of five train journeys from London to Manchester were 2 h 15 min, 2 h 18 min, 2 h 22 min, 2 h 19 min and 2 h 21 min.

For questions **4** and **5**, estimate the mean by using mid-interval values.

**4** Mike recorded the midday temperature outside his house during April. This is a frequency table of his data

| Temperature interval | 5–9 °C (incl.) | 10–14° (incl.) | 15–19 °C (incl.) | 20–24 °C (incl.) |
|---|---|---|---|---|
| Number of days | 2 | 10 | 16 | 2 |

**5** The heights of the students in Class 8A are shown in the table.

| Height interval | 140–144 cm (incl.) | 145–149 cm (incl.) | 150–154 cm (incl.) | 155–159 cm (incl.) |
|---|---|---|---|---|
| Number of students | 6 | 8 | 11 | 5 |

example

There are 240 passengers on a train, 120 of them are sitting in standard class seats, 80 of them are sitting in first class seats and 40 of them are in the buffet car. Display these details on a pie chart.

· · · · · · · · · · · · · · · · · · · · · · · · · · · · · · · · · · · · · · · · · · · · · · · · · · · · · · · · · · · · · ·

For the standard class passengers the angle for the pie chart is $\frac{120}{240} \times 360$ or $180°$.
For the first class passengers the angle for the pie chart is $\frac{80}{240} \times 360$ or $120°$.
For the passengers in the buffet car the angle for the pie chart is $\frac{40}{240} \times 360$ or $60°$.

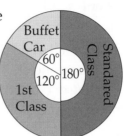

**1** The results of a mathematics examination for the boys and girls in Class 8B are these.
Boys 61  21  73  38  54  29  46  81  24  93  31
Girls 62  54  26  47  73  25  71  55  37  87  65
 **a** Draw a back to back stem-and-leaf diagram to show the two sets of results.
 **b** Find **i** the median **ii** the range for both sets of results.
 **c** Comment on any differences that you notice between the two sets of results.

**2** The table shows the summer sports choices for the students in Class 8A and those for the whole school.
 **a** Display each set of data on a pie chart.

|  | Cricket | Rounders | Athletics | Swimming |
|---|---|---|---|---|
| Class 8A | 4 | 3 | 8 | 9 |
| Whole school | 60 | 90 | 50 | 100 |

 **b** Do Class 8A's choices differ from those for the whole school? If so, how?

example

Joe opened a fish and chip shop at the start of the year and his profits for the first 8 months of the year are shown. Plot these figures on a scatter diagram and comment on the overall trend.

| Month | January | February | March | April | May | June | July | August |
|---|---|---|---|---|---|---|---|---|
| Profit | £550 | £500 | £450 | £600 | £550 | £600 | £600 | £550 |

The overall trend shows that his profits are increasing because the 'line of best fit' has a positive gradient.

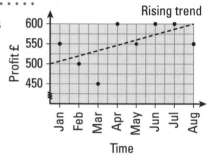

1 The depth of the water in a reservoir is shown for 3 monthly intervals from 2003 to 2007. Plot these figures on a scatter diagram and comment on

|  | 2003 | 2004 | 2005 | 2006 | 2007 |
|---|---|---|---|---|---|
| 1st January | 39 m | 37 m | 37 m | 36 m | 35 m |
| 1st April | 36 m | 36 m | 35 m | 34 m | 35 m |
| 1st July | 29 m | 28 m | 26 m | 25 m | 24 m |
| 1st October | 22 m | 21 m | 21 m | 20 m | 19 m |

**a** the seasonal trend **b** the overall trend.

2 A train operating company records the mean number of passengers that use a commuter train on each day of the working week from 2003 to 2007. Plot these figures on a scatter diagram and comment on **a** the weekly trend **b** the overall trend.

|  | 2003 | 2004 | 2005 | 2006 | 2007 |  | 2003 | 2004 | 2005 | 2006 | 2007 |
|---|---|---|---|---|---|---|---|---|---|---|---|
| Mon | 340 | 350 | 350 | 370 | 380 | Thu | 270 | 270 | 280 | 290 | 290 |
| Tue | 290 | 290 | 300 | 300 | 310 | Fri | 320 | 320 | 340 | 350 | 350 |
| Wed | 280 | 280 | 280 | 300 | 300 | Sat | 180 | 190 | 180 | 190 | 200 |

The best times achieved by four different athletes for the 100 m and 200 m events are shown in the table.

| 100 m time (s) | 11.1 | 11.3 | 11.5 | 11.6 |
|---|---|---|---|---|
| 200 m time (s) | 24.0 | 24.2 | 23.9 | 24.5 |

Plot these times on a scatter diagram and comment on the correlation.

The correlation is positive because the 'line of best fit' has a positive gradient.

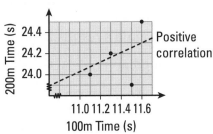

For questions **1** and **2**, plot the data on a scatter diagram and comment on any correlation.

**1** The heights and weights of six men are given in the table.

| Height (cm) | 165 | 170 | 175 | 180 | 185 | 190 |
|---|---|---|---|---|---|---|
| Weight (kg) | 80 | 80 | 90 | 85 | 95 | 90 |

**2** Jean thinks that taxi drivers are more prompt in arriving if they are called out later in the day. She collects the data given in the table.

| Time that the taxi driver was called | 9 a.m. | 11 a.m. | 1 p.m. | 3 p.m. | 5 p.m. | 7 p.m. |
|---|---|---|---|---|---|---|
| Time taken for the taxi to arrive (min) | 13 | 12 | 11 | 7 | 13 | 9 |

example

Ronnie and Josh both claim to be the best sprinter in their class. Here are their times for the 100 m in four recent matches.

Ronnie 11.9, 12.0, 11.7, and 11.6 s
Josh 12.0, 11.3, 11.6, and 12.1 s

**a** Find **i** the median **ii** the mean **iii** the range for each boy.
**b** Comment on your answers.

. . . . . . . . . . . . . . . . . . . . . . . . . . . . . . . . . . . . . . . . . . . . .

**a i** Ronnie's results in order are 11.6 11.7 11.9 12.0, so his
median is $\dfrac{(11.7 + 11.9)}{2} = 11.8$ (Josh's is also 11.8.)

**ii** Ronnie's mean is $\dfrac{(11.9 + 12.0 + 11.7 + 11.6)}{4} = 11.8$
(Josh's is 11.75.)

**iii** Ronnie's range is $12.0 - 11.6 = 0.4$
Josh's is $12.1 - 11.3 = 0.8$

**b** They both have the same median, but Josh's mean time is better. Ronnie, however, has a smaller range so it would seem that his performance is more predictable.

For questions **1** and **2**, find the median, mean and range for each set of data, and comment on your answers.

**1** Anne and Laura both say that they are the best goal scorer for a girls' football team. Here are their records over a five-match cup contest.

Anne 3 1 2 2 and 0
Laura 0 2 2 0 and 4

**2** Zodia and Tnisha both say that they are the best at mathematics in their class. One year they had five mathematics tests and these were their results.

Zodia 80% 72% 68% 81% 73%
Tnisha 77% 73% 83% 71% 70%

**example**

Find the distance from
a Ray's house to the supermarket
b the supermarket to Ray's school.

| Ray's House | | Post Office | Super-market | Ray's School |
|---|---|---|---|---|

1.74 km    1.13 km

← 3.92 km →

. . . . . . . . . . . . . . . . . . . . . . . . . . . . . . . . . . . . . . . . . . . . .

a By partition: $1.74 + 1.13 = 1.74 + 1 + 0.13 = 2.74 + 0.13 = 2.87\,\text{km}$
b By compensation:
$3.92 - 2.87 = 4 - 0.08 - 3 + 0.13 = 1 + 0.05 = 1.05\,\text{km}$

**1** The map shows all the places on a small island and all the roads between them. Given that it is 15.2 km from one beach to the other by either direct route and that the cliffs are both half way between the beaches, copy and complete the distance chart.

East Coast Beach
North Cliff
Northeast Hill
Northwest Hill
South Cliff
Southeast Hill
Southwest Hill
West Coast Beach

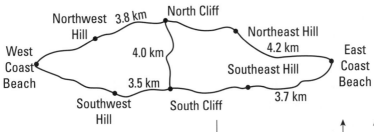

Northwest Hill   3.8 km   North Cliff
West Coast Beach
4.0 km   Northeast Hill   4.2 km   East Coast Beach
Southeast Hill
3.5 km   3.7 km
Southwest Hill   South Cliff

**2** The diagram represents the heights of five members of a family. Given that Wayne is 1.51 m tall, find the height of each of the others.

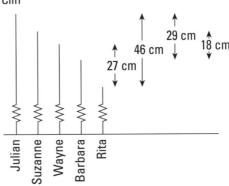

29 cm   18 cm
46 cm
27 cm

Julian   Suzanne   Wayne   Barbara   Rita

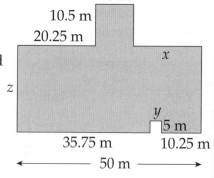

**example**

Find **a** the dimensions marked $x$ and $y$ **b** the perimeter of the shape.

15.15 cm

10 cm

$x$

$\leftarrow y \rightarrow$

6.45 cm

20 cm

. . . . . . . . . . . . . . . . . . .

**a** $x = 10 - 6.45 = 3.55\,\text{cm}$
$y = 20 - 15.15 = 4.85\,\text{cm}$
**b** The perimeter is $20 + 6.45 + 4.85 + 3.55 + 15.15 + 10 = 60\,\text{cm}$.
(Or, more simply, $20 + 10 + 20 + 10 = 60\,\text{cm}$.)

**1** In a lift cage there are eight people whose masses are 70.3, 80.1, 76.3, 69.8, 56.2, 81.5, 78.2 and 60.3 kg. There is also a trolley of mass 288.5 kg which is loaded with three cases whose masses are 51.5, 47.2 and 39.6 kg. On the cage wall there is a notice saying 'Maximum load 1 tonne'. Is it safe for the lift to move?

**2** The dimensions of a school yard are shown in the diagram. If the perimeter of the yard is 195 m, find the distances marked $x$, $y$ and $z$.

10 m

10.5 m

20.25 m

$x$

$z$

$y$

5 m

35.75 m

10.25 m

50 m

**3** A battery is being charged and the table shows the voltages at 10-min intervals. Find the voltage increase for each of the intervals.

| Time (min) | 0 | 10 | 20 | 30 | 40 | 50 | 60 |
|---|---|---|---|---|---|---|---|
| Voltage | 0 | 0.25 | 0.40 | 0.75 | 0.95 | 1.05 | 1.50 |

Plot these details on a suitable graph.

**example**

A trailer has a mass of 2.5 tonnes when empty and a mass of 3.2 tonnes when carrying a flock of sheep.
If the average mass of each sheep is 25 kg, how many sheep is it carrying?

The total mass of the sheep is $3.2 - 2.5 = 0.7$ tonnes or 700 kg.

Therefore the number of sheep is $\frac{700}{25} = 28$.

**1** A train consists of a locomotive of mass 100 tonnes and 10 coaches of mass 30 tonnes each. If it is carrying 400 passengers of average mass 70 kg, what is the total mass moving?

**2** A ferry boat has a mass of 5000 tonnes. If it is carrying 50 cars of average mass 2.52 tonnes and 200 people of average mass 70 kg, what is the total mass afloat? If the load depresses the boat 1.75 m into the water, what is the depression for each tonne carried?

**3** A party of 50 pupils and 3 teachers plan to go on a school day trip. The train fare is £39 for each pupil, £59 for each adult and the school bursar says that £2200 can be made available. Can they afford to go? If so, by what margin?

**4** A book has a mass of 300 g and the mass of its cover is 25 g. If the book has 550 pages, what is the mass of each page?

**5** Jim has a torch battery with a life of 4.5 h. He uses it to walk home from the nearest bus stop, and the walk takes 18 min. How many times can he use the torch for this walk before he needs a new battery?

**example**

Long Avenue is 1.56 km long and there are lamp posts from one end to the other that are spaced 65 m apart.
Find the number of lamp posts.

65 m

Long        Avenue

1.56 km

· · · · · · · · · · · · · · · · · · · · · · · · · · · · · · · · · · · · · · · · · · · · · · · · · · · · · ·

The number of spaces = 1560 ÷ 65 = 24.
Therefore the number of lamp posts = 24 + 1 = 25.

**1** Larch Avenue has eight lamp posts from one end to the other and they are spaced at intervals of 54 m.

54 m

Larch        Avenue

**a** Find the length of the avenue.
**b** On the other side of the avenue there are 10 trees that are equally spaced from one end to the other. Find the spacing of the trees.

**2** Barbara has a 63 m length of clothes line. She wants to fasten it in between four posts that are placed in a square array of side length 15.5 m. Has she enough line? If so, how much will be left over?

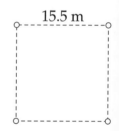

15.5 m

**3 a** Yasmin travels at an average speed of 75 km/h along a motorway for 2 h 24 min. How far does she travel?
**b** Martin travels the same length of motorway as Yasmin in 2 h 15 min, what is his average speed?
**c** James travels the same length of motorway as Yasmin and Martin at an average speed of 72 km/h. How long does it take him?

> **example**
>
> At a supermarket orange juice is sold in 3 different sized cartons. A 1.5 litre carton costs £1.20, a 1 litre carton costs 75 p and an 800 ml carton costs 56p. Which is the best value for money?
>
> .............................................................
>
> For the 1.5 litre carton the cost per millilitre is $120 \div 1500 = 0.08$p.
> For the 1 litre carton the cost per milliltre is $75 \div 1000 = 0.075$p.
> For the 800 ml carton the cost per millitre is $56 \div 800 = 0.07$p.
> Therefore the 800 ml carton offers the best value for money.

**1** Marcus knows that his firm is not doing very well and is expecting to be made redundant. He has, however, saved £240 per month for 6 months to supplement his unemployment benefit. How much per week will he be able to spend from his savings if he is unemployed for **a** 15 weeks   **b** 18 weeks   **c** 24 weeks   **d** 40 weeks?

**2 a** Amir takes part in a sponsored cycle ride from Land's End to John O' Groats and he cycles at 15 km/h for 9 hours each day.
  **i** How far does he cycle in one day?
  **ii** If the total distance is 1620 km how long will the whole journey take him?
  **b** Later Adele takes part in a sponsored walk between the same two places and it takes her 40 days.
  **i** How far does she walk each day?
  **ii** If she also spends 9 hours a day on the move, what is her average walking speed?

# Glossary

| | |
|---|---|
| **algebra** | Algebra is the branch of mathematics where symbols or letters are used to represent numbers. |
| **algebraic expression** | An algebraic expression is a term, or several terms connected by plus and minus signs. |
| **alternate** | A pair of alternate angles is formed when a straight line crosses a pair of parallel lines. Alternate angles are equal. |

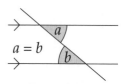

$a = b$

**angle: acute, obtuse, right, reflex**

An angle is formed when two straight lines cross or meet each other at a point.

The size of an angle is measured by the amount one line has been turned in relation to the other.

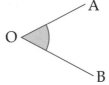

An acute angle is less than 90°.

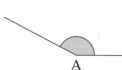

An obtuse angle is more than 90° but less than 180°.

A right angle is a quarter of a turn, or 90°.

A reflex angle is more than 180° but less than 360°.

**angles on a straight line**

Angles on a straight line add up to 180°.

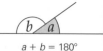

$a + b = 180°$

**approximate**

To approximate an answer is to work out a rough answer using easier figures.

**arc**

An arc is part of a curve.

**area**

The area of a surface is a measure of its size.
Square millimetre, square centimetre, square metre, square kilometre are all units of area.

| | |
|---|---|
| **bar chart** | The heights of the bars on a bar chart represent the frequencies of the data. |
| **base (number)** | The base is the number which is raised to a power. For example in $2^3$, 2 is the base. |
| **bearing, three-figure bearing** | A bearing is a clockwise angle measured from the North line giving the direction of a point from a reference point. A bearing should always have three digits. |

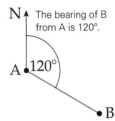

The bearing of B from A is 120°.

| | |
|---|---|
| **bias** | An experiment or selection is biased if not all outcomes are equally likely. |
| **BIDMAS** | BIDMAS is a mnemonic to remind you of the correct order of operations: **b**rackets, **i**ndices, **d**ivision or **m**ultiplication, **a**ddition or **s**ubtraction. |
| **bisect, bisector** | To bisect is to cut in half. A bisector is a line that cuts something in half. |
| **cancel** | You cancel a fraction by dividing the numerator and denominator by a common factor. |
| **capacity** | Capacity is a measure of how much liquid a hollow 3-D shape can hold. |
| **centre** | The centre of a circle is the point from which all points on the circumference are equidistant. |
| **centre of rotation** | The centre of rotation is the fixed point about which a rotation takes place. |
| **circumference** | The circumference is the distance around the edge of a circle. |
| **coefficient** | The coefficient is the number part of an algebraic term. For example in $3n^5$ the coefficient of $n^5$ is 3. |

# Glossary

**collect like terms**  To collect like terms is to put together terms with the same letter parts.
For example $5x + 3x = 8x$ and $4y^2 - y^2 = 3y^2$.

**common factor**  A common factor is a factor of two or more numbers or terms.
For example $2p$ is a common factor of $2p^2$ and $6p$.

**compasses**  A pair of compasses is a geometrical instrument used to draw circles or arcs.

**compensation**  The method of compensation is used to make calculations easier.
For example to add 99, add 100 and then compensate by subtracting 1.

**conclude, conclusion**  To conclude is to formulate a result or conclusion based on evidence.

**congruent**  Congruent shapes are exactly the same shape and size.

**constant**  A constant is an algebraic term that remains unchanged.
For example, in the expression $5x + 3$ the constant is 3.

**construction lines**  Construction lines are the arcs drawn when making an accurate diagram.

**continuous**  Continuous data can take any value between given limits, for example height.

**coordinates**  The coordinates of a point give its position in terms of its distance from the origin along the $x$- and $y$- axes.

**correlation**  Correlation is a measure of the relationship between two variables.

**corresponding**  A pair of corresponding angles is formed when a straight line crosses a pair of parallel lines. Corresponding angles are equal.

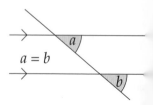

$a = b$

| | |
|---|---|
| **cross-multiply** | Cross-multiplying is a method for removing fractions from equations. |
| **cross-section** | The cross-section of a solid is the shape of its transverse section. |
| **cube root** | The cube root of $x$ is the number that when cubed gives you $x$.<br>For example $\sqrt[3]{64} = 4$, because $4 \times 4 \times 4 = 64$. |
| **cubic** | A cubic equation contains a term in $x^3$ as its highest power. |
| **data** | Data are pieces of information. |
| **data collection sheet** | A data collection sheet is a form designed for the systematic collection of data. |
| **decagon** | A decagon has ten sides. |
| **decimal** | A decimal number is a number written using base ten notation. |
| **decimal place** | Each column after the decimal point is called a decimal place. |
| **degree (°)** | Angles are measured in degrees. There are 360° in a full turn. |
| **degree of accuracy** | The degree of accuracy of an answer depends on the accuracy of the figures used in the calculation. |
| **denominator** | The denominator is the bottom number in a fraction. It shows how many parts there are in the whole. |
| **diagonal** | A diagonal line is one which is neither horizontal nor vertical. |
| **diameter** | The diameter is a chord that passes through the centre of a circle. |

# Glossary

**difference pattern**    You can find a general rule for a sequence by looking at the pattern of differences between consecutive terms.

**digit**    A digit is any of the numbers 0, 1, 2, 3, 4, 5, 6, 7, 8, 9.

**dimension**    A dimension is a length, width or height of a shape or solid.

**direct proportion**    Two quantities are in direct proportion if one quantity increases at the same rate as the other.

**distance-time graph**    A distance-time graph is a graph of distance travelled against time taken.
Time is plotted on the horizontal axis.

**distribution**    A distribution is a set of observations of a variable.

**divisible, divisibility**    A whole number is divisible by another if there is no remainder after division.

**divisor**    The divisor is the number that does the dividing.
For example, in 14 ÷ 2 = 7 the divisor is 2.

**edge (of solid)**    An edge is a line along which two faces of a solid meet.

**elevation**    An elevation is an accurate drawing of the side or front of a solid.

edge

**enlargement**    An enlargement is a transformation that multiplies all the sides of a shape by the same scale factor.

**equation**    An equation is a statement showing that two expressions have the same value.

**equation (of a graph)**    An equation is a statement showing the relationship between the variables on the axes.

**equidistant**    Equidistant means the same distance apart.

**equivalent, equivalence**    Two quantities, such as fractions which are equal, but are expressed differently, are equivalent.

| | |
|---|---|
| **estimate** | An estimate is an approximate answer. |
| **evaluate** | Evaluate means find the value of an expression. |
| **event** | In probability an event is a trial or experiment. |
| **expand** | To expand an expression you remove all the brackets. |
| **experiment** | An experiment is a test or investigation to gather evidence for or against a theory. |
| **experimental probability** | You can find the experimental probability of an event by conducting trials. |
| **expression** | An expression is a collection of terms linked with operations but with no equals sign. |
| **exterior angle** | An exterior angle is made by extending one side of a shape. |
| **face** | A face is a flat surface of a solid. |
| **factor** | A factor is a number that divides exactly into another number.<br>For example, 3 and 7 are factors of 21. |
| **factorise** | You factorise an expression by writing it with a common factor outside brackets. |
| **formula, formulae** | A formula is a statement that links variables. |
| **frequency** | The frequency is the number of times an event occurs. |
| **frequency diagram** | A frequency diagram uses bars to display data.<br>The height of the bars corresponds to the frequencies. |
| **function, linear function** | A function is a rule.<br>The graph of a linear function is a straight line. |
| **generalise** | Generalise means find a statement or rule that applies to all cases. |

# Glossary

**general term**          The general term in a sequence allows you to evaluate unknown terms.

**gradient**          Gradient is a measure of the steepness of a line.

**graph**          A graph is a diagram that shows a relationship between variables.

**greater than or equal to (≥)**    The symbol ≥ means that the term on the left-hand side is greater than or equal to the term on the right-hand side.

**hectare**          A hectare is a unit of area equal to $10\,000$ ($100 \times 100$) square metres.

**hexagon**          A hexagon has six sides.

**highest common factor (HCF)**    The highest common factor is the largest factor that is common to two or more numbers.
For example the HCF of 12 and 8 is 4.

**horizontal**          A horizontal line is parallel to the ground.

**hypotenuse**          The hypotenuse is the side opposite the right angle in a right-angled triangle.

**hypothesis**          A hypothesis is a statement used as a starting point for a statistical investigation.

**identically equal to (≡)**    One expression is identically equal to another if they are mathematically equivalent.

**identity**          An identity is an equation which is true for all possible values.
For example $3x + 6 \equiv 3(x + 2)$ for all values of $x$.

**image**          An image is an object after it has been transformed.

**implicit**          An equation in $x$ and $y$ is in implicit form if $y$ is not the subject of the equation.

| | |
|---|---|
| **improper fraction** | In an improper fraction the numerator is bigger than the denominator. |
| **index, indices** | The index tells you how many of a quantity must be multiplied together. For example $x^3$ means $x \times x \times x$. |
| **index laws** | To multiply powers of the same base add the indices. For example $2^5 \times 2^3 = 2^8$. To divide powers of the same base subtract the indices. For example $5^6 \div 5^3 = 5^2$. |
| **index notation** | A number written as a power of a base number is expressed in index notation. For example $\frac{1}{1000} = 10^{-3}$. |
| **inequality** | An inequality is a relationship between two numbers or terms that are comparable but not equal. For example, $7 > 4$. |
| **infer** | Infer means to conclude from evidence. |
| **integer** | An integer is a positive or negative whole number (including zero). The integers are: ..., -3, -2, -1, 0, 1, 2, 3, ... |
| **intercept** | The intercept is the point at which a graph crosses an axis. |
| **interior angle** | An interior angle is inside a shape, between two adjacent sides. |
| **interpret** | You interpret data whenever you make sense of it. |
| **intersection** | The intersection of two lines is the point where they cross. |
| **inverse function** | An inverse function acts in reverse to a specified function. |

function

input          output
x                   y

inverse
function

# Glossary

**justify**
You justify a solution of a formula by explaining why it is correct.

**less than or equal to ($\leqslant$)**
The symbol $\leqslant$ means that the term on the left-hand side is less than or equal to the term on the right-hand side.

**like terms**
Like terms are terms with the same letter parts.
For example $3x^2$ and $-5x^2$ are like terms.

**line graph**
On a line graph points are joined with straight lines.

**line of best fit**
A line of best fit passes through the points on a scatter graph, leaving roughly as many above the line as below it.

**line segment**
A line segment is the part of a line between two points.

**linear equation, linear graph**
A linear equation contains no squared or higher terms. The graph of a linear equation is a straight line.

**linear expression**
A linear expression contains no square or higher terms.
For example $3x + 5$ is a linear expression.

**linear sequence**
The terms of a linear sequence increase by the same amount each time.

**locus, loci**
A locus is a set of points (a line, a curve or a region) that satisfies certain conditions.

**lowest common multiple (LCM)**
The lowest common multiple is the smallest multiple that is common to two or more numbers.
For example the LCM of 4 and 6 is 12.

**mapping**
A mapping is a rule that can be applied to a set of numbers to give another set of numbers.

**mass**
The mass of an object is a measure of the quantity of matter in it.

**mean**
The mean is the average value found by adding the data and dividing by the number of data items.

| median | The median is the average which is the middle value when the data is arranged in order of size. |
|---|---|
| metric system | In the metric system, units of measurement are related by multiples of ten. |
| mid-point | The mid-point of a line segment is the point that is halfway along. |
| mirror line | A mirror line is a line or axis of symmetry. |

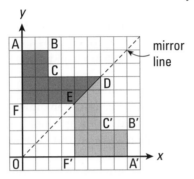

| modal class | The modal class is the most commonly occurring class when the data is grouped.<br>It is the class with the highest frequency. |
|---|---|
| mode | The mode is an average.<br>It is the value that occurs most often. |
| multiple | A multiple of an integer is the product of that integer and any other.<br>For example 12, 18 and 30 are multiples of 6. |
| multiple bar chart | A multiple bar chart is a bar chart with two or more sets of bars.<br>It is used to compare two or more data sets. |
| mutually exclusive | Two events are mutually exclusive if they cannot occur at the same time. |
| negative | A negative number is a number less than zero. |

# Glossary

| | |
|---|---|
| **net** | A net is a 2-D shape that can be folded to make a 3-D solid. |
| **$n$th term** | The $n$th term is the general term of a sequence. |
| **numerator** | The numerator is the top number in a fraction. It tells you how many parts of the whole you have. |
| **object, image** | The object is the original shape before a transformation. An image is the shape after a transformation. |
| **operation** | An operation is a rule for processing numbers. The basic operations are addition, subtraction, multiplication and division. |
| **order of operations** | The conventional order of operations is: brackets first, then indices, then division and multiplication, then addition and subtraction. |
| **order of rotational symmetry** | The order of rotation symmetry is the number of times that a shape will fit on to itself during a full turn. |
| **origin** | The origin is the point where the $x$- and $y$-axes cross, that is $(0, 0)$. |
| **outcome** | In probability an outcome is the result of a trial. |
| **parallel** | Parallel lines are always the same distance apart. |
| **partitioning** | Partitioning means splitting a number into smaller parts. |
| **perimeter** | The perimeter is the distance round the edge of a shape. |
| **perpendicular** | A line or plane is perpendicular to another line or plane if they meet at a right angle. |

| | |
|---|---|
| **perpendicular bisector** | The perpendicular bisector of a line is the line that divides it into two equal parts and is at right angles to it. |

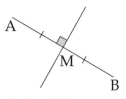

$$AM = MB$$

| | |
|---|---|
| **pi ($\pi$)** | The ratio $\frac{circumference}{diameter}$ is the same for all circles. This ratio is denoted by the Greek letter $\pi$. |
| **pie chart** | A pie chart is a circular diagram used to display data. The angle in each sector is proportional to the frequency. |
| **place value** | The place value is the value of a digit in a decimal number. For example in 3.65 the digit 6 has a value of $\frac{6}{10}$. |
| **plan, plan view** | The plan or plan view of a solid is an accurate drawing of the view from directly above. |
| **plane** | A plane is a flat surface. |
| **plane of symmetry** | A plane of symmetry divides a solid into two halves. |
| **polygon** | A polygon is a shape with three or more straight sides. |
| **population** | The population is the complete set of individuals from which a sample is drawn. |
| **position-to-term rule** | A position-to-term rule tells you how to calculate the value of a term if you know its position in the sequence. |
| **positive** | A positive number is greater than zero. |

# Glossary

**power**
The power of a number or a term tells you how many of the number must be multiplied together.
For example 10 to the power 4 is 10 000.

**primary data, primary source**
Primary data is data you have collected yourself.

**prime**
A prime number is a number that has exactly two different factors.

**prime factor**
A prime factor is a factor that is a prime number.

**prime factor decomposition**
Prime factor decomposition means splitting a number into its prime factors.

**prism**
A prism is a solid with a uniform cross-section.

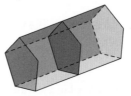

**product**
The product is the result of a multiplication.
For example, the product of 3 and 4 is 12.

**proportion**
A proportion compares the size of a part to the size of the whole.

**proportional to ($\propto$)**
When two quantities are in direct proportion one quantity is proportional to the other.

**prove, proof**
You prove a statement is true by arguing from known facts.

**quadratic**
A quadratic expression contains a square term.

**quadratic sequence**
In a quadratic sequence the second difference is constant.

| | |
|---|---|
| **quadrilateral** | A quadrilateral is a polygon with four sides. |

rectangle    parallelogram    kite

All angles are right angles. Opposite sides equal.   Two pairs of parallel sides.   Two pairs of adjacent sides equal. No interior angle greater than 180°.

rhombus    square    trapezium

All sides the same length. Opposite angles equal.   All sides and angles equal.   One pair of parallel sides.

| | |
|---|---|
| **quotient** | A quotient is the result of a division.<br>For example, the quotient of $12 \div 5$ is $2\frac{2}{5}$, or 2.4. |
| **radius** | The radius is the distance from the centre to the circumference of a circle.  |
| **random process** | The outcome of a random process cannot be predicted. |
| **range** | The range is the difference between the largest and smallest values in a set of data. |
| **ratio** | A ratio compares the size of one part with the size of another part. |
| **raw data** | Raw data is data before it has been processed. |
| **reciprocal** | The reciprocal of a quantity $k$ is $1 \div k$.<br>For example the reciprocal of 5 is $\frac{1}{5}$ or 0.2; the reciprocal of $x^2$ is $\frac{1}{x^2}$. |

# Glossary

**recurring**
A recurring decimal has a repeating pattern of digits after the decimal point,
for example 0.33333 ...

**reflect, reflection**
A reflection is a transformation in which corresponding points in the object and the image are the same distance from the mirror line.

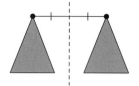

**reflection symmetry**
A shape has reflection symmetry if it has a line of symmetry.

**regular**
A regular polygon has equal sides and equal angles.

**rotate, rotation**
A rotation is a transformation in which every point in the object turns through the same angle relative to a fixed point.

**rotation symmetry**
A shape has rotation symmetry if when turned it fits onto itself more than once during a full turn.

**rounding**
You round a number by expressing it to a given degree of accuracy.

**sample**
A sample is a set of individuals or items drawn from a population.

**sample space, sample space diagram**
In probability the set of all possible outcomes in an experiment is called the sample space.
A sample space diagram is a diagram recording all the outcomes.

**scale**
A scale gives the ratio between the size of an object and its diagram.

**scale drawing**
A scale drawing is an accurate drawing of a shape to a given scale.

**scale factor**
A scale factor is a multiplier.

**scatter graph**
Pairs of variables.
For example age and height, can be plotted on a scatter graph.

**secondary data, secondary source**

Secondary data is data that someone else has collected. Common secondary sources include books, magazines and the Internet.

**sector**

A sector is part of a circle bounded by an arc and two radii.

**segment**

A segment is part of a circle bounded by an arc and a chord.

**sequence**

A sequence is a set of numbers, objects or terms that follow a rule.

**similar, similarity**

Similar shapes have the same shape but are different sizes.

**simulation**

A simulation is an experiment designed to model a real-life situation.

**simultaneous equations**

Simultaneous equations are two or more equations whose unknowns have the same values.

**slope**

The slope of a line is measured by the angle it makes with the $x$-axis.

**solid**

A solid is a shape formed in three-dimensional space.

cube

six square faces

cuboid

six rectangular faces

prism

the cross-section is constant

pyramid

the side faces meet at a common vertex. The base can be any shape

tetrahedron

all the faces are triangles

square-based pyramid

the base is a square

# Glossary

**solution, solve**  The solution of an equation is the value that makes it true.

**speed**  Speed is a measure of the rate at which distance is covered.

It is often measured in miles per hour or metres per second.

**sphere**  A sphere is a 3-D shape in which every point on its surface is equidistant from the centre.

**square root**  A square root is a number that when multiplied by itself is equal to a given number.
For example $\sqrt{25} = 5$, because $5 \times 5 = 25$.

**steepness**  The steepness of a line depends on the angle the line makes with the $x$-axis.

**stem-and-leaf diagram**  A stem-and-leaf diagram is used to display raw data in numerical order.

**straight-line graph**  A straight-line graph is the graph of a linear equation.

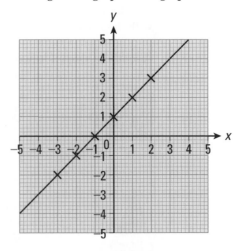

**subject**  The subject of an equation or formula is the term on its own in front of the equals sign.
For example, the subject of $v = u + at$ is $v$.

| | |
|---|---|
| **substitute** | To substitute is to replace a variable with a numerical value. |
| **sum** | The sum is the total of an addition. |
| **supplementary** | You can form a pair of supplementary angles on a straight line. Supplementary angles add up to 180°. |
| | $a + b = 180°$ |
| **surface area** | The surface area of a solid is the total area of its faces. |
| **symmetry, symmetrical** | A shape is symmetrical if it is unchanged after a rotation or reflection. |
| **T($n$)** | T($n$) stands for the general term in a sequence. |
| **term** | A term is a number or object in a sequence. It is also part of an expression. |
| **terminating** | A terminating decimal has a limited number of digits after the decimal point. |
| **tessellation** | A tessellation is a tiling pattern with no gaps. |
| **theoretical probability** | The theoretical probability of an event $$= \frac{\text{number of favourable outcomes}}{\text{total possible number of outcomes}}$$ |
| **tonne** | The tonne is a unit of mass, equal to 1000 kg. |
| **transform** | You transform an expression by taking out single-term common factors. |
| **transformation** | A transformation moves a shape from one place to another. |
| **translate, translation** | A translation is a transformation in which every point in an object moves the same distance and direction. It is a sliding movement. |

# Glossary

**tree diagram**

A tree diagram shows the possible outcomes of a probability experiment on branches.

**trend**

A trend is a general tendency.

**trial**

In probability a trial is an experiment.

**trial and improvement**

Square roots, cube roots and solutions to equations can be estimated by the method of trial and improvement. An estimated solution is tried in the expression and refined by a better estimate until the required degree of accuracy is achieved.

**triangle**

A triangle is a polygon with three sides.

equilateral

isosceles

three equal sides

two equal sides

scalene

right-angled

no equal sides

one angle is 90°

**triangular number**

A triangular number is the number of dots in a triangular pattern:
The numbers form the sequence 1, 3, 6, 10, 15, 21, 28 ...

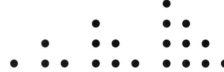

A triangular prism is a prism with a triangular cross-section.

| | |
|---|---|
| **unit fraction** | A unit fraction has a numerator of 1. For example, $\frac{1}{3}$ and $\frac{1}{7}$ are unit fractions. |
| **unitary method** | In the unitary method you calculate the value of one item or 1% first. |
| **variable** | A variable is a quantity that can have a range of values. |
| **vector** | A vector describes a translation by giving the $x$- and $y$-components of the translation. |
| **vertex, vertices** | A vertex of a shape is a point at which three or more flat faces meet. |
| **vertical** | A vertical line is at right angles to the horizontal. |

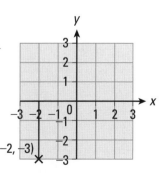

vertex

| | |
|---|---|
| **vertically opposite angles** | When two straight lines cross they form two pairs of equal angles called vertically opposite angles. |

$a = b$
$c = d$

| | |
|---|---|
| **view** | A view of a solid is an accurate drawing of the appearance of the solid above, in front or from the side. |
| **volume** | Volume is a measure of the space occupied by a 3-D shape. |
| | Cubic millimetres, cubic centimetres and cubic metres are all units of volume. |
| **$x$-axis, $y$-axis** | On a coordinate grid, the $x$-axis is the horizontal axis and the $y$-axis is the vertical axis. |

$(-2, -3)$

# Glossary

**x-coordinate, y-coordinate**   The x-coordinate is the distance along the x-axis.
The y-coordinate is the distance along the y-axis.
For example, (-2, -3) is -2 along the x-axis and -3 along
the y-axis.

**zero**   Zero is nought or nothing.
A zero place holder is used to show the place value of
other digits in a number.
For example, in 1056 the 0 allows the 1 to stand for
1 thousand. If it wasn't there the number would be 156 and
the 1 would stand for 1 hundred.